Arthur Gary C
Manchester. Th
can no longer
previously a produce manager for a
supermarket.

He and his wife, Sylvia, have two sons, Gary
and Adam.

This is his first book, but he is already writing his second, not bad for a man who taught himself
to read by bringing stock down from the warehouse to
fill the shelves, and taught himself maths by playing
darts.

Campbell was born and still lives in _____. The rigours of MS have meant that he _____ work, except at his writing, but he was _____ to become _____ well-known _____

Tap-Dancing's Out Then?

A.G. Campbell

By Gary Campbell

First published in paperback in Great Britain by AG Campbell, 2001.

This revised edition published in 2002 by
CK Publishing Ltd,
151, Brookfield Road, Cheadle, Cheshire, SK8 1EY.
Tel: 0161 491 6074
admin@ckpublishing.co.uk
www.ckpublishing.co.uk

ISBN 1 903674 12 3

Printed and bound in Great Britain by
Cox & Wyman Ltd, Reading, Berks..

Syl-Vest

This book is dedicated
to my loving wife,
Syl 'Vest' Campbell.

Multiple Sclerosis Society

Multiple Sclerosis is the most common neurological disorder among young adults - around 85,000 people in the UK have MS. MS is the result of damage to myelin - a protective sheath surrounding nerve fibres of the central nervous system. When myelin is damaged, this interferes with messages between the brain and other parts of the body.

For some people MS is characterised by periods of relapse and remission, for others it has a progressive pattern. For everyone, it makes life unpredictable.

The MS Society is the UK's largest charity dedicated to supporting everyone whose life is touched by MS. Providing respite care and holiday homes, a freephone MS helpline, grants for home adaptations and mobility aids, education and training, specialist MS nurses and a wide range of information. Local branches cater for people of all ages and interests and are run by people with direct experience of MS. The Society also funds over 70 vital MS research projects in the UK.

You can help by:

- Becoming a member
- Making a donation
- Offering your time as a volunteer

Contact the MS National Centre on: 020 8438 0700
National Ms Helpline: Freephone 0808 800 8000
Website: www.mssociety.org.uk

Chapter One

It all started in 1983, on the May Bank Holiday weekend. I had just had a long, hard week at work; I worked for a large supermarket in Sale, Greater Manchester, as a Produce Manager. All that week I had been dragging my right leg behind me, I had hurt it the previous week in an argument over darts in a local pub.

I thought nothing of it really, but then it started getting so bad that I had to have a word with the nurse at work about it. She thought that I had sprained it and so put a cold-water bandage on to ease the pain and told me to see my doctor.

The week had dragged. It seemed like it would never end. I was starting to feel so very tired and my right hand had a really strange sort of pins and needles in it. I was slowing down and I felt so weak. People around me thought that I was coming down with a virus that was going around and would say things like, "You look like you're coming down with the flu." or, "You look rough, boss.".

Now this sort of feeling was all new to me as I was very seldom ill, so I took it as being just that: the flu.

I got home from work on the Saturday night just as my two sons were finishing their tea. All I wanted to do was sit in the chair and have a drink but the two lads had other ideas. Gary, who was the eldest at three and a half, had his favouite Superman suit on. He and Adam, who was fourteen months and toddling, wanted me to play in the garden so I went outside with them to play until tea was ready.

Gary wanted me to pick him up and pretend that he was flying. This was something that we often did so I went and picked him up but as I did I went dizzy and fell onto the grass. The lads thought that I was playing and started to play-fight with me but there was no playing in me. I just lay there on the grass till my wife, Syl came out and told me that tea was ready. Syl asked me if I was OK. I looked up and replied, 'Yes, it's just been a long week.'

I then got to my feet and went in to have my tea.

My mother had come round to babysit for us as we always went out on a Saturday night to the local pub, but for once we decided to stay in and have an early night. I was really starting to feel tired and weak so we bathed the lads and put them to bed. A bit later Syl made me a hot toddy then the three of us settled down to watch a video.

I seemed to pick up after that and went out for the last pint and to get a Chinese meal for us, we even had a bottle of wine and some lagers to wash it down so the night didn't turn out so bad after all.

Mum only lived around the corner but always stayed until Monday morning with us, plus we had a lot planned for that Sunday. I had a darts match to play for the Super League then I was going to take us all to the fair in the park.

I had a good sleep that night and woke up early to have a bath and get ready to go to my darts match. I got in the bath and started to wash myself down but I couldn't feel the water on my legs. It was as if I had two pairs of pants on over them. The pins and needles in my hands were worse so I shouted for Syl and she came into the bathroom and asked me what was wrong. I told her about the pins and needles and not being able to feel the water on my legs. She told me to go back to bed and she would phone for the doctor to come out. I was beginning to think it was more than just a dose of the flu that I had as it took me ages to get dressed.

In my left eye there was a sort of a blur, the kind you get when you rub your eyes first thing in the morning when you wake up.

I went downstairs to the kitchen; my mum was having her breakfast with the lads. I sat down and lit up a cigarette; I went to pick up the cup of coffee that Syl had made for me and nearly dropped it on the floor. This time my mum told me to go back to bed and to get the doctor out, but I said, 'No, I'm going to darts.'

Not long after that my mate Dave called for me to walk down to the pub. Syl told him I wasn't feeling too good and that I needed to stay in and see the doctor. I took no notice and went out to play my darts match.

We were going to our local, the Royal Oak, for a couple of pints and a practice before we went to the match. Now the Royal Oak was only a three minute walk away normally but it took us a quarter of an hour. I had to lean on Dave for support and I was dragging my right leg even worse than usual. Dave kept asking me if I was OK. I told him that I would be when I had a pint or two.

We got to the pub just as they were opening. Dave went to the bar to get the beer while I went to put our names down for a game of darts. I let on to some of the lads and walked over to Frank and paid my "subs", then I went to the bar where Dave was standing.

The pint that Dave had got me was right in front of me. I went to pick it up with my right hand and missed: I had no co-ordination. I tried again and missed. I squeezed my hand tight. It was like I had been lying on it, the pins and needles were that bad. I picked up my pint with my left hand and there was no problem at all with that one. Then I got a call from the lads at the dartboard that it was my turn to mark the board. I went to pick up the chalk and dropped it on the floor. Bending down to pick it up I went dizzy just like I had in the garden. Dave picked up the chalk and said, 'Anything to get out of marking the board as usual, Gaz?'

I wasn't for once trying to get out of marking it, just looked that way. I sat down and started to rub my eye. Dave asked me if everything was OK, as I had gone white. I said that I was fine and he marked the board for me while I sat down until it was time for me to get up to play my game. I went to the oche, faced the board and threw my dart, and it just missed one of my mates who was standing near the board.

'Oi! The board's over there, Gaz,' he said.

'How did you get on the darts team throwing like that?' one of the other lads said, laughing.

Dave walked over to me and said, 'I'll get Woody to give you a lift home. It's silly you going to darts if you are like this.'

I told him that I would walk home as the fresh air would do me good and with that I left the pub.

It was a quarter past twelve. I didn't get in the house till gone one o'clock. I must have looked drunk as a couple of lads I knew passed me and made some comments about the way I was walking. 'You been out all night then, Gaz? It looks it, the way you're staggering.'

The other one sniggered and said, 'Wow! You're in for it when Syl sees you in this state.'

I couldn't blame them for thinking I was drunk, especially with the way I was falling in the hedges and stumbling all over the place. Then, when I finally did get in the house Syl had to help me sit down in the chair. I was so weak my body felt as though it had just been on a ten-mile run, and I just flopped into it. Syl made me a cup of coffee but when I went to pick it up I couldn't. My hand just kept missing it every time I tried.

After a short while in the chair I was starting to feel worse so Syl had to help me upstairs to the bedroom then she phoned for the doctor. She even had to help me unbutton my shirt and other clothes as my fingers just couldn't do it.

I was really scared. I had always been quite fit. OK, I was no athlete, but I played football and the job I did kept me on my toes, so all this illness was something new to me. After a short while the doctor came. I didn't know what to expect when Syl showed him to the bedroom where I was. He walked over to the side of the bed and asked me about my symptoms as he began to examine me.

He did the usual things at first like taking my temperature and my pulse. I was so scared, it must have been racing. After doing my blood pressure he went to his bag and got from it a long, thin object with a round, flat rubber bottom. He said, 'I'm going to test your reflexes. Just relax.'

I lay on the top of the bed while he ran the pointed end of the instrument up and down my feet. He asked me if I could feel anything.

I had feeling in my left foot but my right foot was another matter: I could feel nothing. He asked me to close my eyes and tell him which toe he was moving and whether it was moving up or down. Again there was no problem with my left foot but I never knew whether my toe was being moved up or down on my right. He was a really friendly sort and tried to put me at ease with everything he did. His name was Doctor Clancy, and we had once been on his books many years earlier. He asked me to sit on the side of the bed and to close my eyes as I held out both arms in front of me. I did this for a few seconds then he told me to open my eyes. My right arm had fallen so much so that it was almost touching my legs but my left arm was where it should have been, still straight out in front of me. I'd had no idea that my arm had fallen; I couldn't feel a thing, I thought that they were both where they should have been: straight out in front of me.

He looked at me in a very sympathetic way and said, 'Didn't you know it had done that?'

I started to panic. Syl sat on the bed next to me holding my hand as I asked him what was wrong. He said nothing for a moment and then asked me to touch my nose with my right hand. Again, it was no problem with my left, but as soon as I tried to do it with my right hand I nearly poked my eye out. 'Oh, shit! What is it?' I shouted. Syl put her arm around me and pulled me close to her. Doctor Clancy looked at us and again I asked him what he thought it was.

For a few seconds there was this deafening silence then he reluctantly said, 'I think you may have something called Poliomyelitis.'

That was it! 'Polio! Polio! No way! No way!' I said. I was crying like a child. The tears were streaming down my face, and through their misty glaze I could see Syl, her emotions clearly visible.

'I can't have Polio. No way! I've got two kids who need me!' I blurted out, I just could not believe that I was so ill, I felt my life running away from me. Syl was next to me, the tears running down the sides of her face. She was always so strong and never showed her emotions.

Doctor Clancy put his hand on my shoulders and said, 'We need to get you to hospital as soon as possible.'

Syl and I sat on the bed while Doctor Clancy went downstairs to phone for the ambulance. We didn't know what to say to each other so we just sat there with our heads resting together. The little figure of our son, Gary, came through the bedroom door. He walked over and climbed on the bed and put his little arms around us both and asked us why we were crying. What do you say to a three year old? Syl just said that I was ill and had to go to hospital for a few days to get better. She took Gary back downstairs while I lay on the bed looking up at the ceiling, the tears running down my face.

My mum walked in and she was crying. She sat on the bed and pulled me close to her, the tears streaming from her eyes. 'Oh, son! Oh God, Gary,' she said. 'Don't worry.' And she held me tight, just like when I was a little boy.

Doctor Clancy walked back into the room and told us the ambulance was on its way and it would take us to Wythenshawe Hospital. Mum went downstairs and Syl came back up and sat next to me on the bed. She asked Doctor Clancy what would happen at the hospital. He was putting all his instruments away in his bag when he stopped to answer her question. He told us they would do more tests and take a closer look at me. He was so nice and he looked so sorry for us. He told me he would give me a letter to take with me to the hospital, and told me to give it to the doctor who saw me, and with that he started to write the letter.

I turned to Syl, looked at her and said, 'It can't be Polio. It can't be.' I started to cry again, I just couldn't stop myself. Syl tried to console me but I was way past that stage.

It didn't take long for the ambulance to arrive. The ambulance-man asked me if I could walk down the stairs or would I need to be carried. Well my pride said, "Yes, I could walk", but my legs said "No", so I was carried down the stairs and in to the waiting ambulance.

Syl had made arrangements for one of my mum's neighbours to take her home and sit with her. Syl's sister, Joyce, who only lived round the corner was going to mind Adam.

Neither of us drove, so Syl was going to follow the ambulance in a taxi with little Gary.

A lot of our neighbours were at their gates wishing me the best of luck as I was put on to the waiting ambulance. I kissed my mum and told her not to worry, then I kissed Syl and the lads and I told her I would see her at the hospital. The doors of the ambulance closed. My heart started to beat faster and faster, I didn't know what was in store for me. The engine of the ambulance started, I swallowed deeply, we were on our way to the hospital.

I was taken to the Accident and Emergency Department of the local hospital where I was placed on a bed and wired to a machine. There were two nurses and a doctor in the room. After making me comfortable the nurses took my temperature and blood pressure. The doctor was reading the letter from Doctor Clancy. He walked over to me, smiled, and told me his name, which I immediately forgot as I was too busy watching what was going on around me.

He was very pleasant and tried to put me at ease. He asked

14

me how I was feeling and told me that my wife and son were outside in the waiting room. Straightaway I asked him if I could see them. He said that I could as soon as I had had a few tests done and had answered a few questions. I asked him what the machine was that I was attached to. He said it was to monitor my heart rate and not to worry, as it was fine.

I turned to him and, trying to make light of it, said, 'Well at least something works, then.'

Just then another doctor walked in and spoke to the first one. They stood over the other side of the room talking for a while looking at the letter and over at me.

They walked over to me. The first doctor looked at me and said, 'We're going to move you to another room so we can examine you.'

With that they spoke to the nurses and left the room. One of the nurses started to remove the wires from my chest and place them back on the machine. She was very nice and told me that she was going to bring my wife and son in for a few minutes, leaving the other nurse to tidy up.

As I lay on the bed looking round I saw Syl and Gary through the clear rubber doors hurrying towards me. Syl came over to the bed and asked me how I was then kissed me. Gary was shouting, 'Hi dad! Hi dad!'

Syl picked him up and put him on the bed next to me. I held Syl's hand and told her what had been happening and the nurse came back into the room and said, 'Right, Mr. Campbell, we are going to move you down the corridor to another room.'

The other nurse helped her to move the bed, with me on it, into a much smaller room. We were in the room for a couple of minutes talking and I was laughing at something that Syl had said when the doctors walked in.

'Oh, feeling a bit better now are you, Mr. Campbell?' One of them asked me.

'A bit,' I replied.

'Good. We're going to ask you a few questions now.'

Syl gave my hand a squeeze and said to them, 'Is it OK if we stay?'

They looked at each other and one of them said, 'For now.'

The second doctor came over to me and asked me how the

15

symptoms started. I told him what had happened, and that it had been within a week that all the different things had gone wrong with me.

I told him how I had banged my knee and seen the nurse at work and that she had thought I had sprained it and put a cold-water bandage on it to take away the swelling.

He took a look at it and said, 'Then what?'

I told him how hard I was finding it to walk without dragging my right leg, and he asked me if I was able to walk now. I said that I could, but only just.

With that, he asked me to show him how I walked. I swung my legs over the side of the bed and tried to stand, but went dizzy. The other doctor grabbed my arm and sat me back down on the bed. 'Just give yourself a few minutes,' he said.

I sat there on the bed for a minute then tried again. This time I took a few steps towards the other doctor. He was watching me dragging my leg. 'Right, Mr. Campbell, now turn around and walk back and sit on the bed,' he said.

As I got back on the bed he walked over to me and said, 'Fine, Mr. Campbell, now we're going to examine you.'

'Gary.'

'Sorry?' He said, looking at me.

'My name is Gary.'

'OK, Gary, I'm just going to test your reflexes.'

He had one of those long, thin instruments with the rubber bottom on, like the one Doctor Clancy had used on me.

I looked at the instrument and smiled. He asked me if I had seen one of them before. I told him what Doctor Clancy had done and asked him if he would be doing the same sort of thing. 'Yes, more or less the same thing.'

'OK, Doc! Let's do it.' I said.

He laughed and started to test my reflexes. Each time he did something he would ask the other doctor to do the same thing and then they would compare notes.

'Right, Gary, any weakness in your arms?' Doc asked me.

'Yes. My right arm is really weak and shaky, and my fingers have a sort of pins and needles in them.'

The other doctor took hold of my right hand and asked if I could feel him touching my fingers.

'Not really,' I said.

'Squeeze my fingers as tight as you can, for me,' he instructed.

I could hardly grip them, let alone squeeze them. 'What is it, doctor? Is it Polio?' I asked, praying that the answer would be, "No.".

'We don't think it's that,' he replied.

'Then, what is it?' I asked him, feeling as though my life had just been given back to me.

'We aren't sure yet. We need to do a lot more tests before we can say for sure.'

By this time little Gary was getting very restless. He had been at the hospital for a couple of hours and was thirsty and hungry. Syl said she would take him for a walk and get him something to eat and drink. She asked if it would be all right if they came back in when they got back and the doctors said that would be fine.

When Syl and Gary left, the doctors asked me if I would like a drink. I said that I would, so they organised a cup of coffee for me while I sat there on the bed answering more questions about my arms and drinking my coffee.

Doc asked me if my arms felt weak all the time. I told him no, it was only my right arm and only when I picked something up.

He then asked me to close my eyes and touch my nose with my left hand.

No problem.

But, just as before, at home, when Doctor Clancy asked me to do it, my right hand had a mind of its own. It didn't matter how hard I tried, I just couldn't do it. They asked me to try to do it while I was standing, but it was as if I was going to fall the minute I closed my eyes. Both doctors helped me to sit back on the bed and made more comments to each other.

'Right! Now, can you hold out your arms in front of you with your eyes closed!' Doc asked me.

The same thing happened again, just like when I did it for Doctor Clancy: my left arm stayed where it should but my right had fallen.

'Okay, Gary, this time can you just do it with your right arm and leave your eyes open?'

I did it again, only this time I was watching my right arm fall even though I was putting in every ounce of effort I had to hold it up.

'Please, Doc! Tell me what it is,' I said, feeling really low and totally drained. He looked at me long and hard. I knew he had a good idea but he needed to be sure.

'We really can't say at this stage, as we need to get you on to a ward and do some more tests,' he said in a very sympathetic way.

'I can't stay in hospital tonight, not while my wife is so upset,' I said.

Both doctors tried to tell me how important it was that I stayed and went on to a ward, but I just kept on saying, 'No!'

Doc then left the room, shaking his head. The other doctor kept trying to persuade me to stay, once again, but I just kept saying no.

Syl and Gary came back into the room. She was crying and said to me that I was to stay in hospital. Doc had spoken to her and told her how important it was that I stayed and was admitted to a ward.

'No, I'm coming home tonight, I'm not staying,' I replied. I told Doc that I wasn't being deliberately awkward, I just needed to see my family home safe then I would go into hospital and have done whatever needed doing. Doc said he had arranged a bed for me on a ward and told me how really ill I was and that I would be making a big mistake by going home.

I said no once again and they could see that I wasn't going to stay that night, so the doctors looked at each other, had a quick chat, then Doc said, 'We need to look in your eyes and if all is well you can go home till morning.'

I felt a lot better knowing I would be able to see Syl and the lads safely home.

The doctors took turns to look in my eyes. Doc told me to close my left eye and tell him how many fingers he was holding up. I had no problem I could see fine with my left eye. Then he asked me to close my right eye and tell him how many fingers he was holding up. It was like I had a mist in my eye, just like when you rub them and try to see. I got it all wrong; I said two when there were three and three when there were more.

Doc sat on the bed next to me. He asked me, once again, to stay in hospital, but I looked at Syl and Gary and said, 'No. I'll come back in the morning.'

The doctors finally agreed to let me go, on the strict understanding that I was to report to the ward the following morning.

I agreed.

It was, by now, well past nine o'clock at night and we were all very tired and in need of a drink. We got a taxi just outside the main doors and headed home. I was so unsteady on my feet that it took Syl and the taxi driver to help get me in the house. Then, she made us a drink while I phoned Joyce to bring Adam home.

I next phoned my mum and told her what had happened at the hospital. She was relieved to hear that it wasn't Polio, as first expected, but very worried that they didn't know what it was. We spoke on the phone for a while and she wanted to come round but it was too late for her to be out, so I said that I would see her when she came to see me in hospital. Well, I suppose this is where I get my stubbornness from, because no sooner had I put the phone down than she was knocking at the front door.

Joyce brought Adam back home and we all chatted for a while about what had gone on. Joyce wished me well for the next day then went home. Shortly after that we all went to bed.

That night Syl and me just lay in bed talking about what had been happening that day. Have you ever noticed how time flies when you don't want it to? Well, we had no sooner gone to bed than it was time to get up. Syl made us both a coffee and we sat in bed drinking it. I didn't want to get up. I just wanted it all to be a dream. I still had the blur in my eye; and my right hand still felt numb. So, all this was real and today was when I had to face whatever this thing was. I was very scared inside but trying to be normal on the outside, and being normal for me is to make fun of things.

We had breakfast - well, another cup of coffee and a cigarette. I kissed my mum, held the lads as tightly as I could, had a last look round the house, then me and Syl got into the waiting taxi and went to the hospital.

Chapter Two

The taxi took no time at all to get to the hospital, as it was Bank Holiday Monday and the roads for once were quiet. The driver dropped us off right at the door. When we entered the hospital, the main corridor, usually full of people, was empty, and we asked at the Porter's desk where the ward was. It was right down the corridor next to the Children's Ward.

As we were walking down the corridor, Syl was linked on to my arm to steady me and help me walk. My nerves were really bad. That disinfectant smell that you get in hospitals was getting to me and my stomach was turning over and over. I wanted to turn round and go back home, but this thing that I had - whatever it was - wasn't going to go away without help and that was why I was here: to get that help.

After quite a few stops to rest, we reached the ward and went to the Sister's office. She was very nice and told us that they had been expecting me and showed me to my bed. It was in a room with four beds, the other three already taken.

I sat on the bed talking to Syl while she was unpacking the things I had brought with me.

A nurse then came and asked me to put on my pyjamas. Well, I didn't wear pyjamas and all I had was a pair of shorts and a T-shirt. She said that it would be OK to wear them and pulled the screen round so I could undress and get into bed, which I did with a little help from Syl. When I was in bed the nurse took my temperature and blood pressure and told Syl she would have to leave as the doctors were on their way up to see me.

I was feeling very weak and tired through not sleeping the

night before, so I just lay in bed holding Syl's hand till another nurse came with a trolley full of instruments and again asked her to leave. I kissed my Syl goodbye and she started to cry. That was it, my eyes went misty too, and my throat tightened. I said, 'See you later, Vest, don't worry.' She gave me another kiss and went out of the ward sobbing.

When she had left I felt really alone and worried about what was going to happen, so I asked the nurse if she could tell me anything. She said that she knew nothing, but the doctors would be there soon and not to worry.

I looked at the man in the bed next to mine, and he said, 'Hi, Gaz! Long time no see, mate.'

'You two know each other, do you?' The nurse asked.

'Yes, I know him from the darts league,' I replied.

As we were talking, Doc walked in and came and sat on my bed. 'How are you today, Gary?' he asked me.

'OK,' I said, feeling a little better for having seen a face I knew.

'Good. We're going to have a look at you again in a minute.' With that the nurse pulled the curtain round the bed again. Doc started to do the same tests he had done the day before and he did them over and over. Then two more doctors came and did the same things.

My left eye was still blurred and my right arm still dropped when I held it out in front of me. Nothing had changed overnight.

They took blood and urine samples and did test after test, and the day just seemed to fly past. By the end I was feeling totally drained and tired. I couldn't believe just how tired I was. I even had a sleep, which was something that I never normally did in the daytime.

Later that afternoon, Doc came back with his boss. They examined me, doing all the same tests again. This time I even managed to walk to show him how my leg was dragging.

Doc's boss stood at the side of the bed and said, 'Right, Mr. Campbell, we have a good idea what it is that is wrong with you.'

My heart was racing. I wanted to know what the problem was but at the same time I didn't. I looked at him anxiously, anticipating just what it was he was going to tell me.

'We think you have something called Multiple Sclerosis, or MS for short,' he said sympathetically. I just sat there on the bed looking at them both.

'Multiple what?' I mumbled and felt a cold shiver run through me.

Doc looked at me as his boss once again told me the name: Multiple Sclerosis. He then went on in more detail about it but I wasn't really listening. I caught the odd word: "Nervous System", "Fatigue", "Weakness", but it all went over my head. He said that there were a few more tests to be done but everything pointed to me having MS. He said that he would start me on a course of steroid injections right away to help me.

I thought, "Great, no problem, they can cure this MS thing", and I started to feel much better inside. I really perked up. How wrong I was!

The two doctors stood at the bottom of the bed talking to each other, then the boss doctor turned to me and said he would see me in the morning and left.

Doc walked to the side of the bed and said, 'Did you understand what he just said to you, Gary?'

I said that I didn't really catch that much, just the part about getting treatment for it.

He sat on the side of the bed and started to tell me just what MS was. He said that the treatment I was going to have wasn't a cure, and as yet there was no cure.

I was really taken aback. I had let myself believe that it could be cured but nobody told me that it could be! It was me, as usual, jumping the gun. I asked Doc if I would be able to walk properly again, and would my arms and eyesight be OK after the treatment.

He said that there was every chance that I would recover but with MS you could never really be sure. He went on to say that there was a lot I could do to help myself.

As I lay there on the bed unable to move I just couldn't think straight. All I could think of was how was I going to tell my Syl. How was I going to tell her that this thing I had, this MS, was with me for life?

Doc sat there on the bed talking to me for a while, telling me about the relapsing/remitting sides of MS. When he left, I just lay there in bed thinking and trying to take in what I had just heard.

It wasn't long then before visiting time, and Syl arrived with

22

the lads and my mum, and they were all full of smiles. Syl sat on the side of the bed while Mum and the lads stood at the end. Syl went to kiss me and I just broke down. She pulled the curtain around the bed and I told Syl and Mum that it was almost certain that I had MS.

I tried as best I could to explain to them what MS was. I told them the best I could: what Doc had told me about the relapsing/remitting side of it and that everyone who suffered from MS had different symptoms.

Syl then said just what I needed to hear. 'We will fight this thing together.'

I didn't know why, but I needed that reassurance. I knew deep down inside of me that nothing would change between us, but I had had to hear those words at that time. I felt so good and the smile was back on my face.

We had a good long chat. The lads had drawn me some pictures to cheer me up and they certainly did that. My mum sat at my side holding my hand and she told me all the local gossip that had been going on that day. When they left I was feeling more like my normal self again.

Doc then came back to give me the first of the steroid injections I was to have. Now, this guy was great. He said to me, as he was about to give me the injection, 'Soon be playing darts again, Gary.'

'I hope so, I really do hope so.' I replied.

That night I had a really good sleep after speaking to the other men on the ward for a while. There was Nipper, who I knew from darts. He was in the bed next to mine and had suffered a heart attack. Nipper was a big man who also had a weight problem. He weighed twenty-odd stones and was having to watch his diet, but didn't he love his food?

Then there was Thomas, a Welshman who was in his seventies. He was a well-spoken, quiet sort of man and he was in hospital for a stomach complaint. And last, but not least, there was Jim. He was also in his seventies. He had had a stroke, which had left him with only the ability to nod his head. We all had a good chat and I told a few jokes, and then they started to talk about their illnesses, which was strange to me, as I knew nothing about mine and nor did they.

The morning seemed to come round quickly. The nurses were giving out breakfasts to the patients, all except Nipper who was "nil-by-mouth"! He watched every mouthful that everyone was eating, even Jim who had to be fed by the nurse. I was going to have a lot of fun with Nipper.

I was sitting up in bed trying to touch my nose with my right hand, but there was no change. I was still missing. I had expected the injection to have worked a miracle and for all the symptoms to have gone. Well, I had been told that it was no cure, but I still hoped that it might have been.

Later that morning the boss doctor was on his rounds with some student doctors. They came to the side of my bed and pulled the curtain round. 'Good morning, Mr. Campbell. How are you today?' he asked.

'Not bad.' I answered. All the students were looking and smiling at me.

'Did you sleep well?' one asked.

'Yes, for once.'

The boss doctor stood at the bottom of the bed reading the chart that the Sister had passed to him. He looked up and smiled at me, said a few words to the student doctors, then said, 'Would you mind if some of my students examined you, Mr. Campbell?'

I didn't mind and they were very nice to me, all except for one - and there is always one. This one was a know-all, weedy little wart who asked me, in a very smarmy way, to squeeze his hand. There wasn't too much of a problem with the left hand but with the right I could hardly grip, let alone squeeze, but it wasn't his hand I wanted to squeeze!

It was the fact that I couldn't do it and the smarmy smirk on his face that got up my nose. When they left I sat there in bed trying and trying to touch my nose and to get my right hand to grip.

Doc came later that morning to give me the second of my injections. He told me that a specialist was on his way to see me. I asked him what I could do to get my hand to grip and he left and came back a few minutes later with a soft tennis ball and told me to practice with that. I spent every spare minute that I had squeezing that ball, just trying to get the power back in my hand.

Just after dinner the specialist arrived on the ward. His name was Doctor Sambrook. He was great and very easy to talk to. He did all the tests that the other doctors had done and told me that I was to have a lumbar puncture and a scan. He agreed with the other doctors that it was MS. We sat there for a while talking, then he went and spoke to Doc at the bottom of the bed, and then they left.

It wasn't long after they had gone that we had our tea and I sat up in bed talking to Nipper about all the tests I was going to have to have done. He was only having a sandwich for his tea but this was the first solid food he had eaten in days. I was having a proper meal but I couldn't eat it all, so I gave Nipper my pudding and a bread roll. He was famished and swallowed it in one go. I've never seen anything like it outside a zoo. This man was a beast when it came to eating. He asked me not to tell the nurse that he had eaten it. I looked at him smiled and said, 'Me, Nipper? No way! Your secret is safe with me.'

I turned away and laughed to myself. Oh, was I going to have some fun with him!

Syl came on her own to visit me that night so we could talk about what had happened that day. I told her about the lumbar puncture and the scan I had to have and that it would prove what the doctors thought: that I had MS.

She said I looked a lot better and I didn't seem to be flopping about as much, and she was right. I was sitting up a lot better in bed and I wasn't as floppy. The injections were working.

Nipper was lying on his bed and Syl looked over at him and turned to me and she whispered, 'Doesn't he look like "Jabba the Hutt" out of the Star Wars films?'

Well, that was it! I just fell about the bed laughing. She was so serious, though, and it was true. He really did look like "Jabba the Hutt". We laughed and talked some more until it was time for her to go. I asked her to bring me some sandwiches and sweets as I was starting to get a bit of my appetite back for the first time in days. I was now beginning to look on the bright side for a change.

The next day I had to have the lumbar puncture. It wasn't as bad as everyone had told me it was going to be. I just had to lie flat in bed for 24 hours after I had it. The boss doctor came to see me with the students and the little weedy wart was there again, and once again I couldn't squeeze his hand. And once again, on his little weedy, warty face was that smarmy, smug look. Oh, this guy was really getting up my nose. I don't think I have ever been so wound up. In a way I suppose he spurred me on because I really worked hard to squeeze the tennis ball that Doc had given to me. And it was working, and working well. I was able to feel things again and the pins and needles were no longer as bad. I no longer felt as though I had gloves on and the way I felt in myself, oh! I just cannot describe it.

The treatment was working. I was feeling hungry all the time, due to the steroids, and I was eating all the food that was put in front of me. I was even asking the nurses to bring me food from the staff canteen. Poor old Nipper. He would watch me eat every mouthful and I was really mean and used to eat it slowly in front of him just to tease the hell out of him.

That night Syl came with the lads. It was so good to hold them and feel them next to me and she brought a lot of sweets and crisps for me, and some sandwiches for Nipper.

The following day I had to go Withington Hospital for the brain scan. I was there the whole morning having the tests done and, yes, they did find one: I did have a brain. Now I would find out just what it was that I had. No more guessing, this was it.

When I got back on the ward they were having dinner. I had just had mine when the Ward Sister came and told me that Doctor Sambrook was on his way to see me. He arrived not long after. Doc was with him and they had the results of the scan with them. This was it: the moment of truth. They told me what they had expected - they told me that the scan showed I had MS.

This may sound stupid but I was glad - no, not that I had MS, but I now knew the name, for sure, of the thing I was going to have to fight. They said that I took it well. Well, if the feeling of your world caving in and your stomach in knots is taking it well, then I must have, but all I knew was that this MS wasn't going to get me on the cheap; it would have one hell of a fight on its hands.

I think from that moment on I changed in the way that I looked at life and the way that I was going to live it. The two doctors left and I sat on the bed talking to Nipper about how I was going to get myself fit. Doc came back not long after to give me my injection. I told him how I felt inside. He said that it was understandable to feel that way and that I came across as a strong-minded person, someone who would cope.

I said, 'Looks like I'm responding to the treatment, then?'

'Yes, you're doing well,' he replied.

'Is there a chance of it returning and affecting my walking and hands again?' I asked.

He looked at me and said that with MS you never can tell.

'Well, tap-dancing's out then!' I said, smiling at him.

He shook his head, ruffled my hair and said, 'What a thing to say!'

Doc left after we had a chatted for a while. It was now teatime and Nipper had got some good news: he could start having small portions. It was like giving a donkey strawberries! The food that had been put in front of him was gone in seconds and he was now looking at mine. I gave him my pudding, then I thought that I would slowly walk down to the dayroom to have my first cigarette in days.

It took me a long while to get there. I was stopping and starting and holding on to the wall for a bit of support but eventually I made it and sat in one of the chairs. The cigarette tasted great. I was just sitting in the chair smoking when another male patient walked in, sweating.

He said to me that he was very thirsty, so I said to him that I'd got some cans of lager in my locker and did he want one. He said that he shouldn't but if I was having one he would have some of it, too. So, I went back to my locker, got one of the lagers and took it back to the dayroom. We sat there talking about this and that and shared the lager. Then he just stood up and left. I thought that I had said something wrong, so I just sat there and lit another cigarette.

The next thing I saw was nurses running past the door so I went to take a look. The man was on the floor having what looked like a fit. Beside him was the can of lager that I had given him. I asked the nurse what the problem was, and she said that he was a diabetic and that he shouldn't have been drinking lager. Oops! I told her I had given him the lager and that I didn't know he was diabetic. And he hadn't said that he was.

Thankfully he was OK. I went back to my bed and told Nipper what had happened. I said that I had thought that I was helping the bloke. He said that he was thirsty so I'd shared the can of lager with him.

'No harm in that,' Nipper said.

When Syl came that night I told her about the tests and that they now knew for certain that I had MS. She had spent most of the day at the library looking up anything that she could find on the subject of MS, which wasn't a lot.

She said that she could see a really big improvement in me from the previous day. We had a good laugh about this and that as we sat there and I gave her another big food order. She said that I wouldn't eat that much, but I said it wasn't for me but for Nipper, who was looking as we talked about food. You could almost see his mouth drooling.

The following morning I woke early so I could have a shower before breakfast. This was the first shower that I'd had since I had been in there as I had only been having strip-washes before. I was very nervous about it, as I just didn't know what to expect. I turned the shower on and realised that I could feel the water on my legs. Oh, what a feeling! To feel the water on my legs was wonderful. Now I was feeling a lot more like my old self again. It was great not to have that terrible feeling of having two pairs of pants on and to be able to wriggle my toes again was a dream come true.

After my shower I felt clean and ready for the day ahead. I had my breakfast and did the exercises on my hand. I could squeeze the tennis ball a lot more easily now and I was able to touch my nose with my right hand nearly every time. I was really improving and it showed. I closed my eyes and held my arms out in front of me. After a few seconds I opened my eyes, just enough to peep through. 'Oh yes! Oh yes! I'm back!' I shouted like a big kid. I just couldn't stop myself. From the look on his face, Nipper must have thought that I had gone mad. I didn't care. I was getting my life back. I felt like the lads at Christmas when they open their eyes to find all their presents.

I couldn't wait to tell Syl. I phoned straight away. She was getting the lads their breakfasts and she was crying on one end of the phone and I was on the other, both of us were so excited and thankful for what had happened.

When Doc came I just couldn't wait to show him what I could do. He said that I was responding well to the treatment and that I shouldn't overdo it and should take things easy, as it was still early days.

'When can I go home, Doc?' I asked him.

He gave me a puzzled look. 'Not for a while yet, Gary. You have to have a lot more treatment still, and that decision will have to come from my boss.'

Well, the boss doctor wasn't coming till the next day, but I wasn't really that bothered, to tell the truth. I was on the mend and that was all that mattered. I didn't want to undo all the good that had been done.

The next day it seemed like every student doctor came to see me, either to ask me questions about my MS or to do some tests. It was great. I was walking a lot better, I wasn't dragging my leg as much, and by the time that Syl came to visit that night I was on top form. Mum and the lads were with her and Mum sat there holding my hand telling me all the local gossip, then I played on the bed with the lads. I really showed off that night as it felt so good to be able to do these things again.

When everyone had gone and we settled down for the night I opened the food that Syl had brought in. Nipper sat up in his bed waiting to be fed. She'd brought loads of food in for us. I passed Nipper some sandwiches and some of the sweets. They didn't last very long and he was now looking at mine. I passed him some of mine then I had a walk down to the dayroom for a smoke. I got talking to a few people in there and the time just flew past.

When I went back to my bed the rest of the lads in the ward were asleep. Nipper was lying on top of his bed, snoring his head off; so much so that I couldn't get to sleep. So I got out of bed and, for a joke, went round all the bins to find what sweet papers and crisp packets I could, then put them in Nipper's locker and in his bed. I even put some crisp crumbs round his mouth and on his pillow. It looked like the bloke had gone on a binge; I then went back to bed and went to sleep.

The nurses woke us the next morning by opening the curtains. I lay there for a minute then the nurse asked me if I would like a drink, and I said that I would have a cup of coffee. Then she went over to Nipper to ask him but he was still asleep. She spotted the crisps around his mouth and on the pillow; she looked and saw the sweet papers in his bed. She looked in his locker and found all the sweet papers I had put in there, and she went totally crazy, and I mean crazy! She went a lovely shade of red.

She asked Nipper just what he thought he was playing at, eating all that food. He looked at her, not knowing what she was talking about. She then pointed to the empty packets.

'They're not mine,' he said.

'Oh yes! Well whose are they, then?' Nipper looked right at me.

'It's him! He's at it again.'

The nurse gave me a really hard stare and said, 'Was this you?'

What had started out to be a joke was now looking like trouble. Trouble that had my name written all over it!

I looked at her and said, 'I thought it was all right to feed him.'

Talk about not being a happy bunny. Nipper went crazy! I tried to tell the nurse that I was only joking but she wasn't satisfied that it was a joke and went and told one of the doctors, who later put Nipper back on "nil-by-mouth" for his own good.

Oh, Nipper was not at all a happy bunny and I think if he could have got hold of me he would have eaten me.

Later that day I was moved to the Children's Ward across the corridor. Well, it wasn't strictly a children's ward, as such, but a ward that did tonsil operations and nearly everyone on it was a child.

They said they needed a bed and I was the only one fit enough to be moved, but I think it was because of all the things that had happened since I had been on the ward.

I was on that ward for two days and it was great. I got on well with the staff and helped out when I could, but when I was put back on the old ward Nipper was still not happy with me. It took me ages to get round him. I think that if he could have got out of that bed I would have had it. But, as soon as I said the magic word: "food", he was as nice as pie.

It was the weekend and was very quiet on the ward. I hadn't seen Doc for a couple of days, as it was his time off, so when he came to give me my injection he really did see a difference in me. I was walking very well and I could touch my nose with either hand now without any problem. He tested the strength in my arms and hands and he was surprised at how well it had improved. I told him that the boss doctor hadn't come to see me and he said that it was because I had been moved to the other ward. I asked him if I could go home but he said that I still wasn't right yet.

Syl came with a few of our friends that Saturday afternoon. It was nice to see them. We talked about darts and how things were at work - the usual stuff - but no one mentioned my MS. I totally ignored the subject. I didn't want to know. So when people asked me how I was, I would say, 'No problems.'

When everyone had gone the day seemed to drag. Jim was sitting in his wheelchair looking out of the window. I asked him if he would like to go down to the dayroom to watch television before we had tea. He nodded, so I pushed him in his wheelchair down to the dayroom and put him near the TV. I sat near him and lit up a cigarette, looked over at him and smiled. It was so sad that he couldn't speak. He must have wanted to say so much. He kept looking at me smoking my cigarette so I asked him if he smoked. He nodded, so I asked him if he would like one if I held it for him.

Jim nodded again. I lit him a cigarette and held it to his mouth while he tried to smoke it. His eyes seemed to light up as I held it to his mouth. 'I bet this tastes good, Jim,' I said to him. 'It must have been ages since you last had one.'

He nodded again, only this time he had a very strange look on his face. I lit another cigarette for myself as I put Jim's out. I wasn't a chain-smoker but I did like to smoke, especially when I hadn't had one for a long time. Jim looked at me, as I was smoking, with expectancy in his eyes. 'Do you want another one, too?' I asked.

His eyes opened really wide. He nodded, so I lit him another cigarette and held it to his mouth. He started to cough and splutter so I patted him on his back but he started to choke. I shouted for a nurse, who was just outside the door, and she came in and sorted him out. 'What are you doing giving him a cigarette?' she asked me.

I told her what had happened - that I was having a cig and Jim looked like he wanted one so I asked him and he nodded.

'That's all that Jim can do: nod!' She said, shaking her head.

'Oh! I'm sorry, Jim. I really am. I just never thought.'

I was a total plonker. I had thought I was doing him a good turn. We went back to the ward not long after. Jim was OK and he kept smiling at me as if to say, "never mind".

Every time I went to the dayroom after that I would say to him, 'Fancy a quick cigarette then, Jim?' His eyes would look to the ceiling and he would give me a wry old smile.

There was only one person left on the ward that I had not done something to and that was Thomas. He must have wondered when it was going to be his turn. We spoke to each other about this and that but that was all. He went home that Saturday, smiling at me as if to say, 'I made it, I'm safe.'

When Syl came to see me on the Sunday she told me just how much I had improved in a week. It was true. A week ago I was so ill I could hardly walk or use my hands, but now here I was, able to walk again and the feeling was back in my hands. I know that steroids are no cure for MS and a lot of people with MS don't respond to them as I did, but for me they had worked and I was grateful because it meant I was able to get back to some sort of normality.

Syl and I had a great laugh that Sunday afternoon. As she left, Doc came to give me my injection and I asked him again if there was any chance that I could go home and right out of the blue he said, 'I want you back here first thing in the morning.'

'Nice one, Doc, you're a star,' I said.

That was it. I was dressed in no time and on the phone for a taxi to take me home for the night. I said to Nipper and Jim that I would see them in the morning, then I headed to the main doors to wait for my taxi.

Syl had only been in the house half an hour when I knocked on the front door. My mum opened the door to see me stood there.

'Hello, Mum, how are you?' I said, smiling at her.

'What are you doing here?' She had a look of total disbelief on her face.

'I live here, remember,' I replied laughing.

'Syl! Syl! Gary's here.' She was shouting as she was doing this little dance. Syl came running to the door; they both stood there with their mouths wide open in amazement.

'Are you going to let me in, then?' I asked.

They both stood there in the doorway as I walked passed them.

'What are you doing home?' Syl asked.

'Doc said that I could come home till morning.' We all walked in and sat there in the living room and I told them what had happened.

We had dinner. It was so nice to be home even though it was just for the day.

Have you ever noticed how things look different when you have been away? The house looked a lot smaller than I remembered. I had only been in hospital for a week but I felt as though I had been away a lifetime. Joyce, Syl's sister, came round to see how I was and a few of our friends and neighbours popped in, too. It was a very busy day and the time just flew past. I was glad to be able to sleep in my own bed again.

I was up early on the Monday morning. I had breakfast with the lads, a chat with Mum and Syl, then kissed them both goodbye and was back on the ward for nine o'clock. I had three more injections to have that week and then it would be down to the boss doctor as to whether I could go home or not.

Wednesday couldn't come quickly enough for me. I had been doing my exercises with the ball to strengthen my hand and I was now touching my nose with either hand every time with my eyes shut. My strength was on top form and my walking was much better. I wasn't dragging my leg and I was ready for the boss doctor and his students.

I was sitting on the top of my bed when they came to see me. This was it! Now I would find out how much he thought that I had improved. They pulled the curtain round my bed as usual and I was asked how I was. I told him I was as fit as a fiddle and raring to go. He smiled and asked me to close my eyes and touch my nose: no problem. Then he told me to hold out my arms in front of me: again no problem. The boss doctor then looked in my eyes and they were fine.

Then it was the turn of the little weedy wart. He asked me if I could squeeze his hand, and he had that grin, the sort that got right up my nose. There it was smirking away on his smarmy, little weedy face. He held out his hand and I took a very, very firm hold and began to squeeze. His eyes started to water and his face started to distort, he let out a little whimper, sort of an, 'Aaaaa!'

'How's that, then?' I asked him, as I was the one who was now grinning from ear to ear.

'Oh! Fine, fine,' he said.

'Can I go home, then?'

The boss doctor smiled and said that I could and that I would be seen as an outpatient in Doctor Sambrook's clinic from now on.

Chapter Three

Within the next eight months I had a total relapse of my MS which left me walking a lot slower, plus the blur was back in my left eye but much worse than before. In fact, it was so much worse that I was finding it hard to see. At times, when I was walking, I would have to hold on to the furniture, or the walls or door frames - anything that would give me support for a few seconds while I got my balance back.

I had come out of work and we had moved house. My sister, Maureen, who had moved out of the area, helped find us a house near her in Denton.

The house was wonderful. It overlooked a school field and there were no main roads, so the lads could play in safety without the worry of cars. The garden at the back of the house was large and the front of the house had three large, long, flag-like steps that led to the front door, which also had a step. Either side of the path was a small front garden with roses and a little tree. We loved it; it was a dream-come-true for us.

Our family and friends helped us to move in. My brother-in-law built a lovely stone fireplace and put up wooden beams across the living room ceiling. We painted it black and white inside and out to give it that cottage look. It really was great, but I could never settle in it as I had left all my friends behind me.

OK, so I saw them most weekends for the first few months after we had moved, but then it got less and less - they had to drive a long way. When they did come, we would go out to the local pubs, play darts and have plenty to drink. And drinking and driving don't mix, so my friends would take it in turns to drive.

We got to April and I was taking driving lessons myself. I had never bothered about driving before. It was something that had never taken my fancy. Our Moie (That's the shortened-down name I always called my sister, Maureen) had talked me into them and I passed at the second attempt.

Now I was able to go to see my mates and finish off the darts season in Wythenshawe. It just wasn't the same, though. Now, I couldn't drink, and my mates talked about things that I didn't know about. They weren't doing it on purpose, it was just because I now lived so far away and I wasn't part of the day-to-day life of the area.

I finished the darts season off for the Royal Oak and never signed on for the summer season, even though it hurt me so much not to. I had played for them for many years and I had won so many wonderful trophies with them.

Then I started to go in a local pub and got talking to some of the darts team who asked me to have a game. It was great, I was starting to like the area and I was asked to play darts for the team. I got on really well with the other team members and made some good friends. I really was beginning to settle down.

After a few months we had really settled down well in our new home. One of the first things that we did was to register with the doctor's. It was a group practice with three doctors: Doctors Hussein, Cummins, and Khan. I took ill and went to see Doctor Khan. My walking was getting worse and I was feeling very low in myself. He examined me and said I needed to see my specialist, Doctor Sambrook, at Wythenshawe Hospital.

He made an appointment for me to see him at his outpatients' clinic within a couple of weeks. He was great. He did all the usual tests, and he prescribed a course of steroid injections for me. The course would be, as before, over ten days, only this time I would not have to go into hospital for them. I would be able to have the injections given to me by the District Nurse at the doctor's surgery.

I started the injections right away and again I was responding to them within a couple of days: I was walking better but only this time I had a limp. We went on holiday and took my mum with us. We went to Rhyl, in Wales, on a caravan site. Syl's mum and dad had a caravan there. The weather was fantastic, and the lads had a great time playing on the beach and such. Syl's mum and dad, Edie and Stan, would take us round the shops and the market. On one particular day we were looking round the shops and I was walking very badly and leaning on Syl for support. Edie went off into this second-hand shop and came out with this walking-stick. She had seen it in the window and went in and bought it for me. 'Here you are, use this,' she said to me.

'I don't need a walking-stick!' I said to her.

Edie was a fantastic person; she wasn't only my mother-in-law, she was my mate. We had a great relationship and she was as straight as you can get. There were no half-measures with her, so when she passed the walking-stick to me I knew that it was time that I had one.

I was holding on to Syl's arm most of the time, anyway, so the walking-stick would stop me doing that. I used it for the rest of the holiday and it made a big difference to me. I was able to stop and lean on it to rest for a minute or two, until my legs were strong enough to carry on.

My mum, Stan, and Edie got on great together. One night, after the club on the camp had finished, we'd all had a few drinks too many and were walking back to our caravans, through the children's play area; my mum and Stan started to play on the swings and the slide.

My mum, who was in her early sixties then, and Stan, who was in his mid-fifties, were like a pair of little kids, running up and down the slide, screaming and shouting without a care in the world, till Edie shouted at them, 'Act your age, not your shoe size! Get off the slide!'

Syl and I were laughing; she looked at us with her fixed stare and told us to sort them out as she was going back to the cara-van, then she stormed off. That did it. I just lay on the grass crying with laughter watching them on the slide playing like a pair of kids.

My mum always said that was the best holiday that she had ever had. It is so nice when both sets of parents get on together, and they did.

That week's holiday was fantastic. I saw my mum smiling again, something that she hadn't done since I was diagnosed as having MS. I saw Syl letting her hair down and laughing and joking with people like she always did. I saw my sons playing together and with other children, running about without a care in the world.

We all had a wonderful time.

I wish that I could go back to that holiday and live that time over and over again.

After being back home for a few weeks I found that I had more and more time on my hands. I would go shopping with Syl just for something to do. I would go round the corner to visit my sister, I would do crosswords and I found that I was brewing up more and drinking more and more coffee, something that I had never done before. I had always been too busy working before and now here I was with nothing to do.

The summer was lovely. Gary and Adam would play football on the school field outside our house and I would go and play a game with them, but then I found that I was beginning to tire very quickly in the sun. OK, people do get tired quickly in the sun but I had always been one of those people who could soak it up, but now just a few minutes out in it and I was as weak as a kitten. I was now having to stay in the shade.

Within a few months my MS was starting to play up again. I went to the doctor's and was told by Doctor Khan to watch my diet. Syl put me on a low-fat one; she stopped me eating things like butter, cheese, and any kind of dairy products. She changed the milk that we drank to semi-skimmed; she stopped me having sugar in my drinks. It was only through Syl that I got to know about these things, while I just went about not wanting to know anything.

I must admit that I improved. Not a great deal, but I wasn't feeling as nauseated all the time and I had that feeling that I was doing something about it, and I found over the next few months that things started to settle down with my MS.

I started playing darts for the Mason's pub and I was able to stand up to play a game without too much trouble. What I did find, though, was that I was going to the toilet more often than normal, even though I was only drinking the same amount as I usually did. Sometimes I found that I was just making it to the toilet in time. I just wasn't able to hold out as long as I could before.

We had a lovely Christmas and started the new year of 1985 off well. It was in the early part of the year that I had to go and see Doctor Sambrook again over my MS. He gave me another examination and told me that my MS had got worse since the last time I'd seen him. He prescribed another course of steroid injections to help me through the attack and this time I put on a lot of weight.

I was like the Michelin Man off the TV adverts. I just ballooned out, and I was eating large meals with snacks in between. I used to say that Nipper could eat, but now here I was doing the same. I used to be on the skinny side but that had gone; the steroids were giving me such an appetite.

Throughout 1985 I had to fight to keep my weight down and the weight was winning. I wasn't what you would call fat, but to me I was. People said how well I looked with the extra few pounds of weight I had put on, but to me the weight was a problem.

Then towards the end of the year I had a bigger problem. I was beginning to become incontinent.

I went to bed one night and all was normal. As usual I had had a couple of drinks of coffee earlier, then I went to sleep. I woke up to find myself wetting the bed. I jumped out of bed as fast as I could, which for me wasn't that fast.

'Oh God!' I said as I ran into the toilet. I went back into the bedroom after having a strip-wash. 'I'm so sorry, Syl.' I was so ashamed of myself.

Syl was already changing the covers on the bed. 'Don't worry, love,' she replied, sympathetically.

I didn't know what else to say. I just hung my head in shame. We got back into bed and Syl put her arm around me. I lay awake all the rest of the night, hoping I wouldn't take short again. After that night I was careful of how much I drank before I went to bed, as I didn't want that to happen to me again.

The next time that sort of thing happened I was in the pub playing darts. I had a faded pair of blue denim jeans on, and I sat down to have a drink of my beer and a cigarette. Then I stood up quickly, as I thought that someone had spilt some beer or something on my chair, but nobody had spilt anything. It was me! I was wetting myself. I sat down as fast as I could, hoping that nobody had seen me. I pretended to drop a pint of beer on my lap. It was the only thing I could think of. I remember making a joke out of dropping the pint on myself and laughing at it. But all I could think of was getting home and how ashamed I was. I just didn't know I was doing it at the time.

I walked to the vault door and said goodnight to my mates. The back of my jeans were soaking wet from where I had wet myself and the front of my jeans were just as wet from the beer I had spilled on them.

It took me ages to get home and it seemed that every kid in Denton was out that night staring at me. One lot of kids shouted after me, 'Ha! Look he's pissed himself.' But that's kids for you.

I got in the house and just broke down, I was so ashamed of myself. I went to the doctor's the very next day.

You didn't have to make an appointment back then. I saw Doctor Hussein who was very understanding. I told him that at times I could not control my bladder and it was getting more and more frequent. He told me that it was part of my MS, and arranged for a male nurse to come and see me.

It was weeks before the male nurse finally came out to see me. He was a nice person who explained quite a lot to me. He told me about things called leg-bags, but at that time I thought that I didn't really need them so I was back to square one!

I would have to be on my toes, literally, and watch the amount that I drank. I was glad to see the back of 1985; it had been a nightmare year.

1986 started off well. I had made it through Christmas without any embarrassing moments and was able to enjoy all the festivities, such as having a drink with family and friends. But I found that I watched everything I was drinking. I found myself going to the toilet not long after I had just been, just to be on the safe side. I was getting paranoid over the thought of wetting myself again. As soon as I went to family or friends' homes I first paid a visit to their toilet then I would limit myself to only one drink. At times people must have thought I was being funny with them, not having another drink in their homes. It was making me worse, all the worry of it. I couldn't even bring myself to tell my mum or sister, I was so ashamed. Only Syl and I knew, which made it very hard.

The first my mum knew about it was when I was backing my car on to the drive and I was taken short. She saw me run from the car, its engine still running, my pants soaking wet and me holding my groin trying not to pee. I came down the stairs after having a bath and looked at Mum, her eyes filled up with tears as she looked back at me. 'I just can't control it at times, Mum!' I said to her.

She never said a word. She had a way of making things OK with just a look; a look that only your mother has.

This terrible thing was running my life and this to me was the worst thing that the MS had done to me. I had fought it all the way and I was doing well, but now I had no sense of bladder control and all my self-confidence was quickly going because of it.

I asked to see the male nurse again. It was a different one this time. He thought that it was time I started to use this thing called a leg-bag. He showed me how to put it on. I was really taken aback by it. I still thought that I would have been given a tablet or something, something other than this, something that would control my bladder. But there wasn't anything - this was it!

It was a bag that looked like one of those that have blood in them for transfusions. It had a tube on it that you put a sheath on, then the sheath went over the penis, then the bag was tied to the leg.

There was no glue or adhesive on the sheath. It had to be held on with Micropore (a kind of tape), which was not too safe to say the least. The first time that I put it on I was so ashamed. Syl walked into the bathroom as I was putting it on and I went crazy at her. It wasn't that I was mad at Syl, I was just so embarrassed at her seeing me this way. My pride had just gone right out the window when she'd walked in on me, but she really gave it back to me. Syl pulls no punches. She said that this was the way that it was going to have to be, so let's get on with it. She was right! This was how it was going to have to be if I wanted not to wet the bed again or to have any kind of social life without worrying all the time.

The night that I first wore it in bed I put my pyjamas on. I never wore them normally but I had to hide the leg-bag. I didn't sleep that night through worrying, worrying that it might come off, so I put the Micropore right round the sheath tight, and I mean tight! I wasn't going to get any kind of sleep knowing that it could come off at any time and I would end up wetting the bed.

I was starting to have a terrible time with the leg-bag. It was constantly slipping down my leg and I had no confidence in it. I would tie the ties round my leg and put double knots in them, but they still moved, so in the end Syl bought some wide, loose elastic instead of the ties. This did the trick and it stayed in place much better now. The only problem was the sheath, which always had a habit of coming off, and I was making myself sore by putting the Micropore on too tightly. Through that I found that when I took the sheath off, the end of my penis had gone purple!

I was in a mess, and a terrible lot of pain, but the pain wasn't as bad as the embarrassment of wetting myself. Syl made an appointment for me at the doctor's so he could take a look at it for me. I was so embarrassed by it! I said to him, as a joke, 'Can you take the pain away but leave the swelling?'

We had a laugh but then I was told just how stupid I had been. I have a great relationship with our doctors and I always have done, since day one of me being on their books. They are so helpful and understanding with me.

The male nurse was asked to come and see me to help me with the bags again. He came within a few days and I told him what I had been doing. He showed me a similar way but not as severe as what I had been doing. I also told him that now, at times, I was being taken short more during the daytime and just making it to the toilet.

He asked me why I didn't wear the leg-bag all the time and I told him that when I was in the house I was OK, I could just get to the toilet in time. It was just on the odd occasion that I didn't. He asked me if I had ever worn pads. I didn't know what he was talking about. Pads? He said that around the house, and just as a precaution, they would give me that added protection if I did take short. I didn't want to try these things but in the end, and after a lot of persuasion, I said, 'OK. Let's try them! Anything for me not to have to wear the leg-bag all day.'

The next day he came with the pads and some special underpants you put them in, and he showed me how they went.

When he left I went upstairs to try them on. 'Oh, my God!' I said, laughing uncontrollably. I had looked in the dressing table mirror at myself wearing them.

'Vest! Vest!' I shouted.

'What's up!' Syl shouted to me up the stairs.

'Quick! Come and see this.' She ran up the stairs as quickly as she could. 'Look, Vest. I look like a Sumo Wrestler.'

She stood in the doorway with her hands over her mouth. I could see her trying to stop herself from giggling out loud.

'Oh! Oh! They're OK!' she said, the tears starting to run out of her eyes.

'Behave yourself!' I said, and with that we both fell about laughing.

'Well, if they help you, Gaz, who cares. Only you and I will know, anyway,' she said.

Don't get me wrong! These things are great, and they help

41

people, but for that minute I just could not stop laughing at myself in them. That fat belly that I had, hanging over these white things that looked like a nappy made me look like a Sumo Wrestler. I wore them a few times but they weren't for me, so I asked to see the male nurse again.

He told me to wear the leg-bag for going out and in bed, which I was doing at the time, but if I wasn't going to wear the pads there was nothing else. Well, I wasn't going to go back to the pads so I would have to look for something else myself.

That night I had a darts match so I thought that I would give the leg-bag a try out. I had only really worn it for bed, so this would be a good test. I got ready and put the leg-bag on and made sure that it would not come off! I really put the Micropore on tight, very tight. I was told not to put it on too tightly but I had to be doubly sure. Anyway, it was only for a couple of hours till I played my darts match at the local pub.

I started to walk to the pub and after only walking a couple of hundred yards I felt as though there was something wrong. I stopped and looked down at my legs. The leg with the leg-bag on had swollen up, and I had put the sheath on so tight it was blowing up the bag on my leg as I walked. I looked round to see that nobody was looking, bent down, lifted up the leg of my jeans, and undid the drainage valve on the bag. I squeezed the bag and the air just came whooshing out.

I closed the valve and started to walk to the pub. I got a few more yards down the road then the same thing happened: the bag started to fill with air. This time I was on the main road and people I knew were not far away, walking towards me.

That was it: panic set in. I had the valve partly open and when they got up to me my heart was racing! I was panic-stricken!

'OK, Gary? Off to the pub?' One of them asked.

'Yes, I've got a darts match,' I replied in a sort of high-pitched voice.

'Are you OK? You looked as though you were having trouble walking.' The other one asked in a caring way.

'Oh, no! No! I just stopped for a minute that's all,' I replied.

'Going to the Mason's, Gary?'

'Yes,' I said and I knew what was coming next.

'We'll walk down with you. We're going in there, too,' he

said.

My heart stopped. I knew it. I just knew it. I smiled, then very gingerly started to walk towards the pub. I could feel the bag filling with air. I tried to walk as though to bang the air out of the bag with my other leg. God, I must have looked like I needed the toilet really urgently. I could hear the air making a very strange noise as it was escaping from the bag. I started to whistle to disguise the noise. They looked at me as if I was daft. They tried to make conversation with me on the way but all I could do was this silly walk and whistle.

We got to the pub and when I went into the vault and they went into the other room I was so relieved. I went straight to the toilet and sorted out the bag and as I opened the toilet door to go back into the bar one of the men I had walked down with was waiting to use the toilet. I smiled, mumbled something, and then quickly left.

That night all went well until it was my turn to play my game. My leg used to shake, like when you press on a nerve, and the lads in the pub used to say I was doing my Elvis impression but never really bothered about it. Nor did I. It would usually go off when I put weight on it. But this time it was with me most of the night. I couldn't shift it no matter how much weight I put through it and the stares that I got off people who didn't know me, well! This really got to me for some reason.

But I finally got home and told Syl all about the trouble that I'd had with the leg-bag. Like me, she couldn't stop laughing.

Chapter Four

It was May, our wedding anniversary had just gone and the Bank Holiday weekend was just around the corner. It would be three years that weekend since I was first diagnosed as having MS. We took the lads to Wales for the day. It was a lovely day out for us all and it gave the lads the chance to run off some of their energy on the beach. Little did I know that it would be the last time that I would be able to walk on the beach holding my Syl's hand.

I played a kind of football with the lads. I was really slowing down and I was unable to run or, for that matter, kick the ball. It didn't matter to them. The lads were having fun and we were all enjoying the day. We took them on the fun-fair and they loved it. They were at the ages now to appreciate the fun of the rides and it was showing in their faces. It was a lovely family day out. I got in the house after driving home and just fell into the nearest chair. I was so exhausted, I just sat there for what seemed like ages.

We bathed the lads and put them to bed, as they were dead on their feet, they had played that much. Syl had made us both a cup of coffee and we also then went to bed. I never had the chance to dwell on my MS that day, I was far too busy having fun with my family. Everything seemed, for once, to be going OK but within the next few days I was back at the doctor's. This time over the shaking in my legs.

I was told it was the MS that was causing it and I was prescribed a tablet called Baclofen to help control it. I also told the doctor how my legs were starting to fatigue easily after just small amounts of walking. He asked me if I would like to try some physiotherapy. I said that I was prepared to try anything that would help me to fight back.

A few days later I was in the kitchen making Syl and myself a drink, when the front doorbell rang. Syl went and answered it. I walked into the living room and there stood a lady in a kind of blue uniform.

'Hello. My name is Maureen Butler. I'm the Community Physiotherapist. I've come to give you some physio-therapy,' she said.

Now, this lady was to become my saviour. She would put me on the road to fitness and help me in so many other different ways. But, and I mean but, she was no ordi-nary physiotherapist. Oh no, this lady was the physio-terrorist!

That first day of physiother-apy really showed me up. The things that I took for granted, things that I could once do easily turned out to be so hard. She asked me to show her how I walked, so I did and I thought that I had walked quite well.

Wrong! I was throwing out my right leg instead of what she said was the proper way - walking from the hip; plus I needed a prop-er walking-stick. The one Edie had got me was too small and I was walking with it in the wrong hand.

I was shown some exercises to do. There was one where I had to lie on my back with my knees up, then stretch one leg at a time out to the side as far as I could. Well, after only a few I was feeling it. Maureen told me to do ten on each leg, as slowly as I could. I was able to see from that moment that I had a lot of work to do and it was going to be a long hard job.

After Maureen left I had an urge to do as much exercising as I could. I was given a set of exercises to do each day, something like ten of each of the things that she had shown me, and she told me she would see me in a week.

Some of the exercises I found easy and could do more of, like sit-ups. Instead of doing ten I would do twenty five and I would do these three or four times a day. There were others that I found hard to do, like kneeling on the floor and putting my hands on the top of my chair, then letting my bottom go down a touch, then slowly bringing it back up. I found that this one drove me mad. I couldn't do it properly, as my pelvis and lower-back were so weak. I just didn't realise how weak my lower-body really was; my upper-body was compensating for it and doing all the work, I hadn't noticed it until Maureen had told me. I was getting out of a chair and my arms were doing most of the work, whereas my legs used to.

After just that one visit from Maureen my eyes were opened to what I needed to be doing. All that week I did my exercises. I never cut corners or gave up. It was something that I had to do and it was helping me, it gave me another outlet and I was enjoying doing them in a big way.

Maureen came the following week and she could see an improvement. She gave me some different exercises to do, as the ones I'd been doing were now too easy for me. To strengthen my back I had to lie face down, flat on the floor, with my hands behind my back then lift my head and shoulders off the floor. My God! I could only do a couple and then my head and shoulders only came off the floor a few inches. Maureen said that they had to be a lot higher than I had got them. Then there was "Rover's Revenge", as she called it. I thought that this one was a joke on me, but no. I had to kneel on the floor, as if I was a dog, then like a dog cocks its leg up to pee up a tree, I was to do the same. I felt such a fool, but it worked. It was helping my lower-back and also my legs.

I had a good few exercises now to work with but I found that when I did them on my own I rushed them. I was trying for quantity but I wasn't getting the quality as I had been shown. I thought that the more, the better! OK, I was building up my stamina but I wasn't really getting the best out of the exercises and there was no conning Maureen. Every week she came I had to do them her way, slowly and properly.

Over the next few months I built myself up to a good level of fitness. I had never been so fit and I felt so good inside for it. She got me a new walking-stick and showed me how to use it in the proper way. I was more confident in the way that I was walking.

I was still throwing out my leg but not as much. Now, though, my walking was getting so bad that I could not walk very far. I now couldn't get on the school field and play football with the lads. I was now having to watch them as I sat on the front doorstep.

The days of me being able to play football with my sons had

been taken away from me. Now all I could do was watch them and hope that one day, soon, I would be able to once again run and play football with them.

I was put on another course of steroid injections to help me with my walking but this time they never worked. I was really finding it hard to walk, even though I now had two walking-sticks. The physio-terrorist, Maureen, brought me a Zimmer frame to try out. I was gutted. The thought of now having to use this thing really hurt but it was the only way that I was going to still be able to walk about.

I was able to put it in my car for when we went visiting, as it was a collapsible one. I was OK with it in the house, but there was no way that I could use it to go walking round the shops. I still went to darts, though, and I still played. The lads on the darts team said that I had the heart of a lion. I don't know about that but I do know that I hate giving in unless there is no other way.

Well I played on for a few months more using the frame to hold me up until I just could not stand and throw darts at the same time anymore. I had to give in even though I was still winning. Now I was being clapped not for the way that I played my game but because I was on a Zimmer frame. That, to me, was the time to quit, and it hurt, really hurt. I still went for a pint but it wasn't the same without playing darts.

I went to the Mason's one night and I got talking to the lads in there over darts. I had a few drinks and I forgot that I was wearing a leg-bag. It had filled up almost to the top without me knowing. So when I stood up I thought that someone had a hold of my leg. I had never let this sort of thing happen before. I got hold of my Zimmer frame and slowly walked to the toilet. I had to keep stopping and trying to pull the bag up without drawing attention to it, which wasn't easy. One of the men in the vault asked me if I had hurt my leg. I said, 'No! It's just water on the knee!' And carried on to the toilet.

I had by now got quite used to using the Zimmer frame, and one day Syl put some "Go-faster" stripes on it. I took them off, though, as they made me look like a yuppie!

Syl was having to do more and more for me now. I was having a hard time walking up and down the stairs for one thing. On some days I had to go up on my bum. Syl would have to move my legs up the stairs, one at a time, while I bumped up each one in turn. Not only that but there were times that I could not walk in from my car so I would have to crawl. One day I was walking in the house the back way. This was the only flat level access into the house. I got as far as the kitchen and fell. I had to crawl the rest of the way, as I usually did. I crawled into the living room and pulled myself onto my chair. I had done this several times before and thought nothing of it; it was now a part of my life. The lads were used to seeing me crawl and often sat on my back for a ride. But this day my mum was sitting on the sofa. She had never seen me having to crawl before and though she never said anything I saw her face. She filled up and left the room. It must have hurt her so much to see me having to now do this to get about. My mum often saw me crawling after that, and at times I could see her, just like Syl did, going to try to help me.

Gary and Adam would help me to walk to the kitchen when I had a good day. I would let them hold my arms as if to hold me up. To them this was everything, and to me.

1987 saw me getting myself really fit. My body was now much stronger and I wasn't getting as tired after doing everyday things, like I had been doing. I had built up my upper-body to a good size and was again able to walk, though not too far, and I did use the walking-stick. However the problem arose again of me not getting to the toilet in time. I didn't like to wear the leg-bag all day, it was uncomfortable, plus I wasn't really in need of it in that way. I just needed something that would allow me the time I needed to get to the toilet.

I once again asked to see the male nurse. It was the one that I liked. He was very helpful and told me about something called the penial clamp. Ouch! Yes I do mean, Ouch! It did what the name suggests - it was a clamp that fitted on the penis. When you were taken short you clamped it shut. Ouch!

This quickly stopped you from wetting yourself but it also stopped the blood flowing at the same time. Believe it or not, but this was the answer to my dreams. It would give me the time I needed to get to the toilet and I would not have to wear the leg-bag.

The body of the clamp was made of metal. It hinged in the middle so it could open out and go round the penis. On the end of one side there were teeth, and on the other a slot so that when you closed it, it would clamp shut. Ouch! I was told to never wear it all day; to only clamp it shut when I needed the toilet, and only for short times - enough time to reach the toilet.

Well I did what I was told and it gave me the freedom that I was looking for. I was able to reach the toilet no problem now. Then I had the brainwave: I could use it when I went for a pint or going shopping. Well the first few times it was wonderful, I was now able to stand at the urinal as I used to. When I used the leg-bag I had to go into a toilet to use it. This may sound daft but I felt great standing there using the urinal. I felt as though I was a man again. It's the simple things in life like this that mean so much to me.

I was using the clamp all the time now but when I needed to clamp it shut, I would have to put my hand down the front of my pants to do it. Now, trying not to be seen by anyone was fine most of the time, especially around the house, but on the odd occasion I got some strange looks to say the least. The urge would come and I would panic, my face would distort as I tried to put my hand down the front of my pants; it must have looked very strange. I once did it in the house and my mum gave me a very weird look. I had no choice in the end but to tell her. I ended up telling my sister and all my family and close friends. I didn't want them thinking I was going funny or something. I even told Maureen, the physio-terrorist, about it, because I wore it when I did my exercises.

I had been using the clamp for a good few weeks now and all was going fine. Then I took Syl to the market in Hyde. I drove because, at the time, Syl didn't. I had to stay in the car as there was no way that I could walk round the market on my Zimmer frame. It was far too busy a place.

I had my clamp on as usual and it was a bitterly cold day. I had been in the car for a while when I got the urge to go to the toilet. I pressed the clamp on, as the toilets were too far for me to walk, then waited till Syl got back to the car.

It wasn't long before Syl got back from her shopping and I didn't say anything about the clamp being shut tight as it didn't hurt, so I just drove home. We got home no problem then I tried to get out of the car. I couldn't move. My legs went stiff and it took ages for me to get out of the car. The pain that I had in my kidneys was unbelievable.

I was walking like a robot. I got in the house and told Syl what I had done. She went totally crazy at me. I was now in the house but then came the problem of getting up the stairs to the toilet. Syl said that she would get a bottle for me to use but I was having none of it. I wanted to use the toilet - stubborn as usual.

It took ages for me to get up the stairs to the toilet. I was so stiff that Syl had to help me move my legs step by step. When I finally did get there and took off the clamp it was like a volcano erupting. The urine gushed out of me then just stopped. I had to sit down on the toilet and push my stomach to help myself to finish off emptying my bladder. My stomach went rock hard. Syl read me the riot act and told me, in no uncertain terms, just what a fool I had been. It was the first time that I had ever done it but it wouldn't be the last. I would do it many, many times again.

There were times that I have visited someone and not been able to get up the stairs to their toilet, so I had to clamp it on and take the pain. I would rather do this than to take the embarrassment of wetting myself, or the hassle that it took for me to get to the toilet and the fuss and bother that it caused.

1987 saw me struggling on my feet again. I was still doing my physiotherapy at home with the physio-terrorist but my legs now were not too good. In fact my right leg now hardly had any feeling in it. I could no longer wiggle the toes and I could just about stand on it. It had started to just buckle under me.

I got some push-pull type hand-controls for my car and this made it much easier for me to drive. I'd been starting to struggle driving at times and felt it was dangerous. There were times when my foot would miss the pedal and I had to put it back on with my hand. Not a very nice thing to have to do but now all that was going to be a thing of the past, thanks to the constant moaning and ear-bashing I got from Edie.

I had to go to Withington Hospital for a check-up. I was now finding it hard at times to pass water. One minute I could not stop, and now I wasn't able to go. I went to the Urology Department. I was asked lots of questions by this young doctor, then asked to lie on the bed. He then asked me more questions as he was examining my stomach.

He asked me if I had ever had an internal. I said that I hadn't. With that he pulled the screen round the bed. It was full of whopping great holes. If it had been up to me I wouldn't have bothered pulling the thing round.

I could see Syl, through the holes, looking at me and smiling. I was so nervous and embarrassed. I had never had anything like this done before and I just didn't know what to expect. I was told to take down my pants and underpants then I had to lie on my side with my knees up to my chest. I could feel myself going red. I couldn't see what the doctor was doing. My nerves were going wild so I sort of mouthed to Syl through the screen, 'What's going on?'

She just shrugged her shoulders, smiled, and mouthed back, 'I don't know.'

She was holding back her laughter, I could see that much. Then the doctor said, 'Right, Mr. Campbell, just relax.'

Well, my heart was in my mouth; and you know where his finger was? Yes, where the sun doesn't shine.

I didn't know where to look; I could see Syl breaking her neck to get a closer look.

Then he said, 'Right, Mr. Campbell. Squeeze my finger.'

So I turned round and went to grab his finger with my hand.

'No! Mr. Campbell. With your bottom, please!' he said, smiling.

Oh! I felt such a fool. I looked at Syl. All I could see was an empty chair, but I could hear her crying with laughter just out of sight. The doctor finished his examination and told me to get dressed. Syl popped her head around the screen, her eyes red through crying with laughter.

'Not a word. Not a bloody word,' I said to her. With that we left the hospital and went to visit Syl's mum and dad who only lived down the road.

When I pulled up outside the house I told Syl not to say a word. I should have known better. She is just like me when it comes to having a joke, only this time I was going to be the joke. She ran into the house as quick as she could. She told me that she needed the toilet. I should have known better. It took me a couple of minutes to get in the house and as soon as I walked into the kitchen, where Stan and Edie were, their faces said it all. Syl had told them. Not just them, but also most of her family.

Syl is one of sixteen children and most of them were there that day. Nobody said a word till it was time to go, then Edie said, 'There is a pervert at the hospital, pretending to be a doctor!'

Well that was it; everyone just fell about laughing, holding one finger up in the air. I couldn't stop laughing myself, it was so funny. What a thing to do. Well. When he said, "Squeeze my finger." I didn't know I was supposed to do it with my bum; it was all something new to me. Even now Syl's family laugh at that. If I ever have to have it done again there is no way that Syl is going to be in the same room.

After that examination I was told that I didn't have a problem with my bladder and the amount of water that I was passing was fine. So what was my problem? I tried water tablets to see if they could help. They didn't but cranberry juice did. It was very good, but it also gave me another problem - the runs. So I was back to square one.

Chapter Five

Over the next few months Maureen, the physio-terrorist, found a lot more exercises for me to do, especially on my pelvis. These were to help strengthen my muscles and to help my bladder and these exercises really did help me. I found that doing them each day virtually stopped me from having to push my stomach when I went to the toilet.

The first exercise I had to do was lie on my back with my knees up, then I had to lift my bottom of the floor whilst keeping my back pushed tight onto the floor. I would do twenty-five of these. Next I would kneel with my hands on the floor, just as I would if I was doing "Rovers Revenge", then let my back slowly droop towards the floor and raise my head up; I'd hold it for a few seconds, then raise my back and lower my head so as to look at my legs. I would do twenty-five of these also. I did these exercises two or three times a day. I was really fit and my back was getting much stronger, too.

I combined these exercises with the ones that I already did and would workout each morning for at least an hour. I was able to do at least five hundred sit-ups then without any problems, but no matter how hard I tried I couldn't get my legs to respond.

I sometimes went swimming with the local Multiple Sclerosis Society branch, but now my legs were playing up I couldn't get from where I had to park the car to the baths and still have the energy to go swimming. Reluctantly, I had to stop going.

I found that I wasn't getting out as much now either. OK, I took Syl to the shops, and I picked the lads up from school, but I would stay in the car. I wasn't going round the shops with Syl, or going into school. All I was doing was sitting in the car watching the world pass by me.

I tried so very hard to make my legs stronger. Every spare second that I had I would do some kind of exercise on them. Looking back I can see that I was my own worst enemy. I never gave them the chance to rest. Even when I was watching the TV I would lift them up and down, then take them out to the side. I was so scared that if I stopped I would lose them forever, and I could not stand for that to happen.

I just went on and on, as usual overdoing it, when really just staying on my feet was good enough. I was getting so fed up with not being able to walk round the shops, or look round the market it was affecting me personally. I was getting so short-tempered and ratty with everyone. One day Maureen, the physio-terrorist, came to do my exercises with me. She asked me if I would try out a wheelchair. I was totally gutted at the thought of it but she told me that with a wheelchair I could once again go round the shops. I was very, very reluctant about it, but after a long hard talk and quite a lot of soul-searching I agreed to try one.

It took Maureen a couple of days to borrow a wheelchair for me to try out. She had to borrow one from the local Social Services, just for a few days.

Maureen had done this for my benefit but I was so scared at the thought of having to use a wheelchair. Now I would be able to see for myself just what it was like to be in one. At first when I saw it I refused to sit in it. Then after yet another talk about the benefits that I would get out of using it I did. I sat down in it. This, to me at the time, was giving in, a thing that I had never done.

The wheelchair had four small wheels on it so I was unable to wheel myself around. At first Syl pushed me up and down the kitchen to see what it was like to be pushed. I didn't like being pushed or the idea of Syl having to push me about but there was no other way of doing it. Maureen said that if I liked it she would see about getting me one that I could propel myself.

Well, after a few turns round the garden and in the kitchen Maureen showed Syl how to put the wheelchair in the car. Then came the suggestion that it was a nice day so why not try it out having a look round the shops.

I wasn't too keen on that idea. Oh, no! In the house nobody could see me, only Maureen and Syl, but going round the shops. Well, that was another matter, my pride would take a massive battering if I was to do this.

But that was what the wheelchair was for, for me to use out of the house and round the shops. I finally agreed and Syl put the wheelchair in the car then I drove us to Ashton to have a look round.

Now Ashton was far enough away from our house for there to be little chance of us meeting anyone there we knew, plus Syl and I liked the market. So off we went, and all the time I was driving all I could think of was that wheelchair and having to get in it and be pushed around in public.

It took no time for us to reach the market. I parked the car in one of the back streets and Syl took the wheelchair out of the boot and wheeled it to my door. This was it! There were loads of people about. I stood up ready to sit in it but then I just quickly sat back down in the car. 'What's up, Gaz?' Syl asked me.

'I can't, Syl. I just can't,' I said. I sat there, in the car, looking at the wheelchair and shaking my head.

'Just give yourself a minute, Gaz. It's OK,' Syl said, trying to put me at ease. I stood up again. This time I sat in the chair.

'Oh, God! Everyone's looking at me now, Syl.' Nobody was looking at me, it was just me, I was so scared. People were doing what people do on markets - they were shopping, looking for bargains, not at me in a wheelchair. Syl once again asked me if I was OK. I nodded then she started to push the wheelchair, this time with me in it.

We started out, nice and slowly, looking in the local shop windows first, then we moved over on to the market itself. It was so nice to be out and about again. It had been so long since I had been round the shops.

I could not stop looking for people who were looking at me in the wheelchair. I was looking for an excuse, just the one would do, then I could turn round to Syl and say, 'See! I told you, people are staring at me in this.'

But it didn't happen. No. I had no excuse. People never really noticed me. I was just another person shopping.

After about half an hour I started to calm down. I didn't like the idea of being in a wheelchair, who would? But it wasn't that bad. In fact it was good in a way. I was able to have a good look round the stalls on the market at what was for sale.

I could not get in some of the stalls, though, so Syl had to go and have a look and tell me what they were selling. We got to this certain stall and it was packed with people, so Syl went and had a look. She was gone for ages, then when most of the people moved away, and I could see the stall, there was no Syl! I couldn't see her anywhere. Then out of the corner of my eye I saw her on the next aisle. She was slowly walking along looking at the stalls without a care in the world.

Well there was no way that I could catch up to her. The wheelchair only had small wheels so I was stuck there. I stooped down and tried to move them with my hands but it was no use. A man asked me if I was all right and if I needed any help. How nice of him to offer to help me. Well, this was my chance to go for a joke on Syl. I told him that my wife had forgotten me again, this was always happening, and would he mind going and getting her. She was on the next aisle looking at the stalls. He was really decent and asked me what Syl looked like. I told him and he went and fetched her.

Well her face was a picture. 'Oh, Gaz. I'm so sorry,' she said, cringing. I told the man that she used to do it to the kids when they were babies in trolleys. He just laughed and went on his way. Syl never stopped apologising to me all the way round the market.

We decided to stop and have a coffee. We had to leave the wheelchair at the door, as there was no room for it inside. To get to a seat I had to lean on Syl and use the backs of chairs till I could get sat down. As we were having our drinks we just both burst out laughing at what had happened it was so funny. We had the drinks and I got back in the wheelchair, then we headed back to the car, this time from a different direction.

We got to the road and Syl had to get the wheelchair down a kerb. This was the first one that we had come across, the way that we had come on to the market was flat, so this was all new to us. Syl pulled the wheelchair back towards her so the front wheels were off the ground. My life quickly passed in front of me. Bump! She did it! We were down, no problem. Syl looked at me and said, 'Just like pushing a pram.'

We went towards the car. The ground was full of potholes and guess what, I went down one. I fell out of the wheelchair onto the floor and I just sat there laughing. Syl for some reason had run off about five feet, then turned back, looked at me, then burst out laughing. I got back into the wheelchair and Syl asked me if it had put me off. I smiled and said, 'No.'

The rest of that day all I found myself talking about was the wheelchair, and how it had made life easier. That night Tony, Syl's brother, came round with his girlfriend, Jane. He often came to take me out for a pint. He is my best mate and we have done so many things together over the years, as you will soon find out.

That night he asked me to go for a pint to the local pub and he would push me in the wheelchair. Well I wasn't ready for that then. It was OK going round the market in Ashton, where nobody knew me but going to my local pub was another matter altogether. Tony said that I was being stupid and not to bother what other people thought, but I just couldn't, so I went out as usual on my Zimmer frame.

We got a taxi to the pub. We had a really good night and a few drinks, to boot. Well quite a few to be honest, so one of the lads from the pub dropped us off at the bottom of our walk.

We got out of the car and slowly started to walk to my front door. It was about sixty yards away but my legs were very tired. They just would not walk anymore, so I got on the floor and I said to Tony that it would be quicker if he grabbed my legs, like in a wheelbarrow race.

'No! Get up, I'll hold on to you,' Tony yelled at me.

'No, Tony it will be better and quicker doing it this way,' I tried to explain. Well he came out with a right mouthful and told me that there was no way that he was going to do that.

I said, 'OK, then, I'll crawl.' And I did. I started to crawl down to where our house was.

'No! No! Don't show me up, Gaz,' he said, looking down at me.

Tony and me are very close. I wasn't trying to show him up, it was just that my legs wouldn't work. I started to crawl. That was it. Tony ran to our front door to tell Syl, then ran back and started to walk at my side, all the time going on at me to stop. Just then this lady walked towards us, he looked down and said, 'Not a word! Not a

****** word!'

With that the lady started to pass us and I just happened to say to her, 'It's OK. He's training me for Cruft's.'

The lady laughed. Tony just walked off and I could hear him mumbling under his breath, 'You're dead! You're dead.'

Tony and I are always taking the mickey out of each other and that was a perfect time to get him.

We got in the house, after quite a struggle to get me up the front steps, and just laughed about it all as usual. Now our Tony has got a great sense of humour. It's a good job with all the things that I do to him, but he gets his own back, he really does.

Within the next month Maureen, the physio-terrorist, had got me an appointment to see about a wheelchair. We had to go to Withington hospital to the Artificial Limb and Appliance Centre Unit (A.L.A.C.), where they measured me for it. This time the wheelchair would have two large wheels at the back so I would be able to propel it by myself. I tried quite a few. I didn't realise just how many types of wheelchairs there were. I finally got fixed up with one and was told that it would take about three weeks to be delivered, as they had to be ordered. I was looking forward to it in one way, and then in another I was regretting even going to see about it. But now the decision to have it had been made. To me it was giving in but I had no choice. I needed to get about outside and this was the only way of doing it.

Within a few weeks the wheelchair arrived and I was trying it out in the kitchen. The lads asked me to show them how to do wheelies. I tried and tried but I wasn't very good at doing them, well it was my first day. Syl asked me to take her to the local market in Denton and to try the wheelchair out there. I took her but I stayed in the car. I wasn't ready for that just yet. I needed a bit more time to get used to it first.

Later that day I took us all down to visit Syl's mum and dad to see how everyone was. When we got there, Syl started to take the wheelchair out of the boot. I told her to put it back as I was OK.

We went into Syl's mum's. They were all in the kitchen, as usual. I walked in on my Zimmer frame. Tony and Jane were there. He asked me if I had got the wheelchair yet. Syl told him that it had arrived that morning and it was in the boot of the car. Well everyone looked at me, then Edie said, 'Then why are you not using it?'

'I'm OK. I only need it outside,' I replied.

'Oh, yes! Well then you can come shopping with us instead of sitting in here,' she said smiling at me.

'Oh! No, I'll stay here with Adam,' I said sheepishly.

'Well, dad's coming shopping with us, so get the wheelchair out,' she said with that "do as I say or suffer" look that she had. Syl went out to the car and got the wheelchair. I went down the front step and sat in the waiting wheelchair. I wasn't too keen to be seen in it but there was no getting out of it. Syl and Tony both went to the back of the wheelchair to push me but in the end dad said, 'I will show you how to push it properly.'

He used to work with handicapped children as an ambulance driver, so he knew what he was doing - I hoped!

We got to the top of the road then Syl took over pushing me. I was trying to push myself along at the same time but I kept getting slapped on the back of the head and told, by Syl, to "leave it" so you just can't argue with that.

We went round the local shops in Chorlton. It was like one of those family days out. There was Syl, mum and dad, Tony, Jane, Gary and Adam, and of course me in the wheelchair. Tony and Jane were watching Gary and Adam near the road when we were going to cross it. Syl pushed me in between two cars and out into the road. 'Wow, Syl! Watch the cars,' I said, frightened to death.

'Oh, don't start. How do you expect me to see over these parked cars,' she shouted back at me.

Everyone was laughing. We crossed the road and got on the pavement. Syl ruffled my hair and said, 'That was close, Gaz.'

'Close! Close! Oh really?' I just shook my head and we carried on looking round the shops.

That afternoon was a good learning stage for us because at the end of it Syl became so good at getting me up and down kerbs. I was learning to do wheelies to help her. We were quite good after that first day out. The best thing was that I was able to look at things by myself using the big wheels and Syl could not walk off and forget me again. After that I started going out more in it. First I would only go round Ashton or Hyde, but then one day in Hyde I met some people that I knew.

This was the first time that I had come face to face with someone I knew whilst I was in the wheelchair. I could feel myself shrinking into the chair and looking away as if to try to hide from them but it didn't work. I was cornered with nowhere to go and I had to talk to them. It was a bit strange at first, for both of us. But then, well it was like the wheelchair had vanished. We started to talk then I let my mouth run away with me, as normal. They really did only see me and not the chair. I was being paranoid, like usual, over it. We chatted for a while then went about our shopping. Syl just said, 'Told you there was nothing to worry about.' Once again she was right.

The year was drawing to a close and Christmas was just around the corner. The lads were really looking forward to it. Syl and I had been busy looking round the shops for the lads' presents. That year He-Man toys were all the rage and certain figures you just could not get for love or money.

We went all over Manchester looking for them, but every shop we went into had sold out of them as soon as they went on display. We even had my sister, Maureen, and my mum looking out for them for us.

It was a good job that I had my wheelchair, as there was no way that I could have done that sort of shopping on my Zimmer frame and I didn't want to miss out on it; it's all part of the Christmas spirit, shopping for presents.

It seemed that everyone was out all at once looking round the shops for things to buy.

It was very difficult to get into certain places - there was no access for wheelchairs. This was something that I never really thought about before, as we had always gone to Ashton or Hyde shopping around the markets. I'd never really looked at how I would get into places. Now I found that Syl and I were asking people we knew about different places, and if they had things like disabled toilets and flat access lifts. I was so surprised how many people didn't know.

It's true, though. When I was able to walk I didn't pay any attention to places. I never looked at how hard it would be for someone in a wheelchair to get in or out. It was something that never crossed my mind.

Then we went shopping in Stockport. I was in the wheelchair and loaded up with presents on my knees. I was holding on to the presents so I could not propel myself along. Syl was pushing me instead. We were just about to go through a large glass door in a store when this man in front let it go. The glass door just whacked against the front of my wheelchair. I thought that it would have smashed the glass, it hit that hard. Luckily it didn't. A very kind lady rushed over and held the door open for us to go through. This was the first time that this kind of thing had ever happened to us, but it would by no means be the last. It scares the life out of you when it happens. You just can't react quickly enough when you are seated. I was glad to get all the shopping done and be able to finally enjoy Christmas.

That year was enjoyable for us all. The lads got all the presents that they wanted. It was so good to see their faces on the Christmas morning. We had plenty of people popping in over the holiday and our spirits were high. We had plenty to eat and drink and we forgot about our problems for those few days. We could look forward to a new year and hope that things would improve for us.

Chapter Six

1988 started and I was determined to get myself fit and shed the weight I had put on over the Christmas period. Maureen, the physio-terrorist, was making working-out hard as usual, but I really enjoyed doing my exercises. I was working hard on my arms and upper-body using weights and doing press-ups. I started slowly at first then built up to a really good workout. The weights were five kilograms; I had one in each hand and I would lie flat on my back on the floor with the weights at my side. I then lifted one over my head, then the other, alternating until I'd done twenty-five on each arm.

Then I would lie with my arms outstretched with a weight in each hand, and bring both arms together holding them above my chest for a count of five then put them back down. I would do twenty-five of these also. Next exercise was lying flat on my stomach with my arms outstretched over my head, then I was to lift the weights as high as I could, one at a time. This exercise, I found, was very difficult to do. I could do it but it was a task. Maureen told me to only do five of each but once again I had to do it my way, I just loved to do the exercises.

I would workout with the weights, then do my loosening up and then I would do my workout. All this would take an hour each morning, then I would go about my day-to-day routine of taking Syl wherever she wanted to do her shopping, and so on.

I just wished that the work I was doing on my upper-body, I could have done on my legs to make them stronger, to make them work. It wasn't for the lack of trying, they just did not respond to anything that I did with them.

There was no way I could get my right leg to do anything

like what I wanted it to, in fact I could not feel anything in it. There was, now, very little I could do with it. I did a lot of work on it but I was losing the battle. I was now finding it hard to get around the house on my Zimmer frame; Syl made the suggestion that I started to use the wheelchair instead of the frame when I was having a bad day.

There was no way that I was having that. I just couldn't let myself do that, as I saw it as giving in. I would rather crawl than have to do that. I was still not using the wheelchair locally so when Tony came to take me for a pint I would still use the Zimmer frame in the pub. By now we had to use another pub as the Mason's had steps and I could not manage to climb them, so we started to go in a pub called the Cock, as it had a flat access.

A lot of the lads that once went in the Mason's now went in the Cock so it was like a home from home. There were a lot of times that Tony asked me to use the wheelchair to go to the pub but I just kept on refusing. So, one night in the pub Tony started to talk about my wheelchair in front of some of the lads we knew.

'I didn't know you used a wheelchair,' one of the lads said.

'He's too embarrassed to,' Tony said, smiling at me.

I was really put on the spot by him saying that! The questions were coming thick and fast from the lads, wanting to know why I wouldn't use the wheelchair in the pub.

I came up with all kinds of excuses, like I was OK in here, and I only needed it to go shopping sometimes, but in the end the lads in the pub said that I was being stupid.

Tony loved every minute of it, it was his turn to put me on the spot and didn't he put me right on top of that spot! Well and truly, he did. That night in the pub went well. I was really sorry in the end that I had not, for once, gone out in the wheelchair as it was a long time before Tony and I went for a pint again. Not because of what had happened that night but because he was looking for a house near ours.

When we did finally go for a pint again I went on my Zimmer frame. It was a real hard struggle for me to do it but my pride won again. I was having to put my arms under so much pressure they had to work overtime to hold me up, it really was crazy. At the end of the night when we got in Tony told me that he would not take me for another pint if I did not use the wheelchair. But just like Tony he was there the next night to go for a pint. I told him that I had no money to go out with. 'That's not a problem, Gaz. I will buy you a couple of pints,' he said, grinning.

So I had no excuse. Syl got the wheelchair out of the car, I got in it and then Tony started to push me to the pub. My nerves were not that bad really, I just felt a little apprehensive until we saw some people we knew walking to the pub. They let on to us, then I was OK.

We got in the Cock no problem - it was flat access, no steps. We went into the vault where our friends normally were.

'OK, Gaz?' Someone said.

'I'll just move these chairs,' another said. Everyone there just carried on as normal, there wasn't a problem. The problem was me. I had been making a mountain out of a molehill, just like when I first used it to go shopping with Syl. It was good; I was able to move about with ease. Until, that is, I wanted to go to the toilet. The wheelchair could only get down part of the passage that led to the toilet, so I had to hold on to Tony's arm and use the wall and door frame to get into the toilet itself.

I wasn't able to stand up at the urinals so I had to go into the cubicle and lean up against the wall. I was just locking the door behind me when I heard this sound of metal hitting the floor. I looked at the lock and the little ball of the sliding bolt had broken off. There was no way that I could open the lock now without that. I couldn't see it anywhere on the floor so I shouted to Tony who was only just outside the door.

'Tony! Tony!'

'What's up?' he said.

'I'm stuck, I can't get out.'

'What do you mean, "you're stuck"?'

'Just what I said. I'm stuck. The bolt on the door has broken off.'

'Trust you. Move from the door, I'll give it a shove.'

'No! I'm right behind the door, propped up against the wall.'

Just then, someone walked into the toilets and I heard Tony say, 'Have you got a five pence piece, mate?'

There was a silence, then, 'You don't have to pay to use the toilet mate,' a voice replied.

'No! I know that, it's to open the screw,' Tony yelled at the man.

'Won't it just open?' the man asked.

'No! There is somebody in it.'

'Then you will just have to wait until they're finished!' the man told Tony, who by this time was really getting ratty. I could hear it in his voice.

'No!' he said very sharply to the man. 'There is somebody trapped inside.'

'Ha! Ha! Who is it?' the man asked.

'It's my bloody brother-in-law, Gary.'

'Can't he open it from the inside, then?'

Well that was it. I was crying with laughter by now, trying not to be heard by Tony. The tears were running down my face, I could hardly keep myself upright.

'Are you thick? He's lost the knob off the lock so it won't open,' Tony growled out at the man.

'I'll go and get the landlord, to see if he can help,' the man told Tony.

The next thing I knew, there was a screwdriver being pushed under the door.

'Here, Gaz. Use this to slide open the bolt,' the landlord shouted through the door.

I finally got out after about a quarter of an hour of mayhem.

'Sorry, the bolt is goosed,' I said to the landlord, feeling really embarrassed about it all.

'No problem, Gaz,' he said.

Tony's face was a picture. They helped me to get back in my wheelchair and I went to go back into the vault. Some of the lads from the vault were in the passage, cheering and whistling as I wheeled passed them.

'Using the toilet again after, Gaz?' the landlord asked me.

'More than likely,' I replied.

'Then I will put some sandwiches and a flask in there for you, just in case,' he said laughing.

We had a really good laugh about it all, even Tony saw the funny side in the end. We got in late that night and told Syl and Jane. They, like us, found it very funny. I was the talk of the pub for ages after that night. I was never bothered about using my wheelchair to go in there again.

It was spring and by now I was really fit. I had lost a lot of weight and had turned it into muscle. I was really doing well. The only problem I had, though, was that I crawled nearly all the time round the house and I was having great trouble getting in and out of the bath.

Maureen, the physio-terrorist, asked Social Services to call in and see Syl and myself about how they could help. It was a nice lady called Helen Weberly - she got me some bath-aids to help me with that side of things. There was a wooden seat that went into the water, then another bench-like thing that went across the bath, plus some handrails. One could be put on the side of the bath and tightened when needed. The other handrail was permanently fixed to the wall at the other side of the bath. This made having a bath a lot easier for me, and when someone else took a bath the aids could easily be removed without any fuss.

Now the only other thing that was a big problem was the stairs. I was asked about having a stairlift to help me, and guess what? My pride, and I, refused.

Helen Weberly called in quite a few times to see me over the next few weeks; she had several jobs around the house done to help me, such as handrails in the toilet. These made it much easier for me as I was finding it very hard to stand in there without holding on to something. She kept asking me to have a stairlift fitted to help me get up and down the stairs. She said that it could take years to be done so now was the time to get things in motion, whilst I had the chance.

I really didn't like the idea of having a stairlift in the house; this would be a big step for me to take. I wouldn't even have the wheelchair in the house. I would only use that outside and when I had used it, to go to the pub or wherever, and then came home, I would always get out of it at the door. I just could not bring myself to use it in the house, no matter what.

It took a lot for me to have the bath-aids and the handrails, never mind a big thing like a stairlift in the house, which was now changing in a big way. There was now a visible sign of my illness with these kinds of things being put around the place. I had always tried to hide the fact that I needed help in doing things but now these aids were on show for everyone to see, and it hurt. To have a stairlift on permanent display was the last straw for me. I would rather struggle than have that embarrassment.

The trouble was, I wasn't the only one who was struggling up and down the stairs. My Syl was doing a lot of struggling with me. She was doing a hell of a lot of work with me and it was no easy task for her. She never moaned, she never complained, she just got on with it, so why was I doing all the fussing and moaning? This was going to help me, just like the wheelchair did and I got over that. So I said yes.

Helen suggested that we go and see one working in a client's house. I said that it would be a great idea, so she arranged for us to go and see it. We went a couple of days later to this lady's house. She had a good chat with me and told me how the stairlift had changed her life for the better. She had no more struggling getting up and down the stairs now. She had complete independence again. This was just what I needed to hear - independence: a lovely word, and a thing that I didn't have right now.

The stairs were my biggest problem right now but that could be a thing of the past if I got the stairlift. I tried the lady's model for myself. It was... Well! It was OK, I suppose. But I didn't like the idea of people standing at the bottom of the stairs, watching me going up on this slow-moving chair.

But it was no big deal. In fact, it was a piece of cake. All I had to do was sit on it and press a button. So much easier than sitting on the stairs and moving my legs one step at a time and I didn't need to ask for help from Syl. I did it by myself -independence.

Right! It was wonderful to use this thing in the lady's house, but could I come to terms with it when one was put in our home? Well, that I was going to have to overcome if I was going to progress the way I wanted to. Helen told us that it would be quite some time before we heard anything about the stairlift, so life, as usual, went on as it had been.

It was spring and the lads needed to let off some steam. School had broken up for a couple of weeks, so we decided to take them out for the day to Camelot theme park.

We asked my mum and sister, Moie, to come with us. We had been there before and really enjoyed it. I had a problem walking then and found it very difficult to get about, but now I had the wheel-chair to use.

We got there just as they were opening. There were lots of people already going in. The lads were so excited. I was, too, and now I would be able to get to the places I missed out on the last time we visited. Mum and our Moie had never been before so the lads whisked them off to the stocks to have their photos taken. I was asked to have my photo taken but I refused as I was in my wheelchair. For some reason, I just couldn't bring myself to be photographed in it.

As we went round the park, Mum, our Moie, Syl and the lads were going on all the rides they could get on. I wasn't going on any. I always found an excuse like, "there were too many stairs", or, "it's just for kids". The fact of the matter was, I was scared; scared that I might have held the ride up while they helped me on; scared that people would see me struggling. I did go on some things, though, like the darts stall or the shooting range, anything that didn't bring attention to me.

We were going round the grounds of the park, telling the lads about the legend of King Arthur, when we came across the sword stuck in the stone. We told Adam that the person who could get the sword out of the stone would be the King of England. With that, Adam ran over to the stone and started to try to pull it out. Well he pulled and he tugged, he gave it all that he had. In the end he walked over to us, shaking his head, and said, 'It's no good, they've superglued it in.'

We all fell about laughing at that. He looked at us and said, 'It's true, you have a go!'

I will never forget that day, it was so nice. I just wish that I'd had the guts to go on the rides with them. I so much wanted to, but…

A few days later we took the lads to Blackpool for the weekend, to a holiday village. Edie, Stan, Tony and Jane had arranged to meet us there. They were staying on the same camp but had been there all week. It was wonderful to see the lads really enjoying themselves on all the big rides. At the fun-fair Stan took them in this haunted house. He made them go first, Gary came out and told us.

They wanted to go on almost everything that was there and this time I went on some of the rides with them. And do you know what? I loved it. I was like a little kid myself. This was the time that Syl's mum, Edie, had to use a wheelchair herself. She didn't like the idea, either, but she had a breathing problem so she had to use it to get about. She could walk short distances, that was all. But she was a fighter and didn't she fight it. We had a great weekend. I think that we must have covered the whole of Blackpool, shopping, and there was no way that I could have done it without the wheelchair.

When we got back home I was soon back into my old routine again, doing all my daily exercises. I had neglected doing them whilst we were away and I had a lot catch up on. By now I was only able to crawl around the house, as my arms were hurting all the time through me trying to hold myself up on the Zimmer frame.

My right leg, now, could not support me and my left was giving way after only a few yards, so crawling seemed the best option. The trouble was I was damaging my knees at the same time. There was always a drawback to everything that I tried to do, no matter what. Maureen, the physio-terrorist, would go mad at me. She was constantly telling me to use the wheelchair in the house.

One day I was upstairs, crawling from the bathroom to our bedroom, as usual, when Syl said to me, 'Have you cut yourself?'

There was a trail of blood behind me on the carpet where I had been crawling. I had pulled off a toenail as I was going across the metal strip that holds the carpet down. The toenail was trapped between the metal strip and the screw that held it down. I hadn't felt a thing. The blood was everywhere. Syl cleaned up my toe and sorted it out as best she could. After that she wanted me to stop crawling upstairs, but there was no other way of getting about if I didn't crawl, so this sort of thing happened quite a lot. I was forever falling, or cutting myself crawling. Then one day, out of the blue, Maureen, the physio-terrorist, called in with a chair called a Glider that she had borrowed for me. It was like a normal plastic chair, only with small wheels on the bottom. This was wonderful! I could push myself along using the walls and my feet to move the chair. It was so easy, especially when I had a bath. Our bathroom was very small, just enough room for the bath and a sink. Now I could sit in the chair and get undressed, rather than sitting on the side of the bath.

There were many times that I had fallen off the side of the bath onto the floor when trying to undress, or when I had got out of the bath. Syl even got a folding chair at one stage to see if that would help, but it was too light. Now this Glider chair, well this did a great job!

One night I had just had a bath. I loved to use talc after I'd had one, but this time I'd used loads of it. When I got to the top of the stairs my hands were bright white; they were just full of talc. The lads were in bed so I only had on my bathrobe, nothing else. We had two banisters, one on each side of the stairs, to make it easier for me to get down them. Well I didn't want to get the talc all over them so I thought I'd use the robe to hold on to the banisters. I put my hands in my pockets and went down the stairs with the robe opened out, holding on to the banisters.

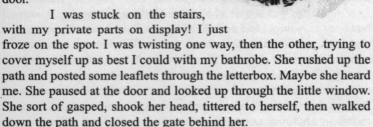

Our front gate squeaked whenever anyone opened it. Just then, it squeaked! I'd forgotten that the front door also had a small glass piece in it. I could see there was a lady just about to come up the path to the front door.

I was stuck on the stairs, with my private parts on display! I just froze on the spot. I was twisting one way, then the other, trying to cover myself up as best I could with my bathrobe. She rushed up the path and posted some leaflets through the letterbox. Maybe she heard me. She paused at the door and looked up through the little window. She sort of gasped, shook her head, tittered to herself, then walked down the path and closed the gate behind her.

The living room door opened and Syl walked into the hall. She was about to pick up the leaflets from the floor when she saw me struggling to walk down the stairs - everything on display and trying to cover myself up. 'Oh, my God,' she said, laughing. 'What are you doing?'

With that I slipped and fell down the last few stairs.

'I didn't want to get talc on the black paintwork,' I explained. Then I tried to sort myself out on the floor.

'You didn't come down the stairs like that did you?' Syl said, all flustered-like.

'Yes, and that woman was looking at me through the little window.'

That did it! Syl went into one of her uncontrollable laughing fits that she has. 'Trust you,' she said, helping me to sort myself out and to get in the living room.

'That's it! I'm getting some net for that little window in the door tomorrow,' I said, still blushing and sorting myself out.

As usual we saw the funny side of it. At times like these that's what we always did. I just hope that the lady who was delivering the leaflets did.

After that I never used talc again and I always made sure that I was properly dressed when I got out of the bath, whatever the time of night.

Later that year I stopped taking the Baclofen tablets; they usually stopped my legs getting too stiff. I thought that it would be better if I had that little bit of stiffness in my legs to help me to walk with my frame again. Well, my legs were better for the stiffness. I could stand on them but the jumping and spasming was back in them when I sat down. They would just go out of control. The lads took it in turns to sit on my knee just to put their weight through them. Even when they did that it did not always work, so I used to cross my legs which seemed to work a little. I would sit there in my chair or wheelchair, legs crossed, looking like Buddha, but it eased the problem so I didn't care what I looked like.

It was the School Sports Day. Syl and I went to watch the lads in their events. This was the first time I had been in school in the wheelchair and I was quite nervous. A lot of Gary and Adam's friends knew I used a wheelchair because they had seen me going round the shops in it, so it wasn't that bad. As I was wheeling myself over to the field where the events were taking place we saw a few of Syl's friends so we went over to where they were. Syl and her mates were talking and they let on to me, as you do, then this little boy looked at me. He was really staring and weighing me up. 'Can't you walk?' he asked.

Well, his mother grabbed him and said to me, 'Oh, I am sorry.'

'There's no problem. He's only asking a question,' I said, laughing. With that the little boy smiled back at me, walked round the wheelchair once more, then started to play around me.

That sort of thing has happened to me hundreds of times and each time I have laughed and joked with the children. They are only being inquisitive and are asking valid questions, so I help all that I can. We were very proud parents that day. The lads won plenty of races and games. Their faces, as they had to go on the stage for their awards, were wonderful. They looked over to where Syl and I were and they had that great look of satisfaction on their faces. My pride to see our sons on the stage, it was just so great. The school broke up a week later and we took them to the American Adventure Park in Nottingham. What a lovely place. All the staff were dressed as

Indians and cavalry. The lads thought that it was fantastic. I was doing well. I felt great. I was in good health for once so I decided not to wear a leg-bag as my bladder was behaving. I thought that I would just use the clamp.

The day was wonderful. I went on some rides and I was able to get into the toilets. There was no problem getting in the café to eat either. Everything was fine; it was a fantastic day. Then we started the long drive home!

I was driving down the M1 back to Manchester when I got the urge to go to the toilet. I needed to pee but there was nowhere that I could pull up. I looked for the sign for the Services but there were none for miles. Syl told me to pull onto the hard shoulder and go behind the car, but I didn't fancy that. I wasn't that bad. I was used to the clamp by now and I could last a long time with it clamped shut, so I carried on. And on, and on, all the way home. Oh, yes, was I sore by the time that we got there.

Syl had to get the wheelchair out of the boot of the car and push me into the house. Then she had to get a bottle as there was no way that I could get up the stairs to the toilet. Then the problem was I couldn't pass water. Usually when I took the clamp off the water would just gush out of me but now I had to push my stomach and it still wouldn't come out. My stomach was as hard as a rock, it took me ages to empty my bladder and the pain was awful. I should have known. I should have played safe and worn the leg-bag. Just because I had a few days without any problems I thought that I would have been fine. It was just wishful thinking on my part.

My MS did this sort of thing to me so many times in so many different ways. I was always hoping that this time would be the right time and I would be on the mend, because that was what I was always working towards. But, so often, this wasn't the case and I ended up in a mess. But I had to carry on trying, I had to keep hoping.

A few weeks later I started having a problem with my right knee. It was very sore and starting to really swell up and burn at times, especially when I had done a lot of crawling around the house or kneeling to do my exercises. I was feeling very poorly as though I had the flu coming on but without the cold. Syl told me to go to bed and she would send for the doctor. The doctor came out and found that I had an infection in my knee and I was taken into hospital to have the inflammation drawn off.

Chapter Seven

I was taken to Tameside hospital and put on a medical ward. There I was examined and placed on a drip, which contained antibiotics to help fight the infection. I had to have the fluid drawn off my knee by a doctor. It really hurt. I was then told just to have bed rest. I settled on the ward in no time.

Now, something that I can do is make friends quite easily and in one of the beds next to me was a very quiet man. He seemed to keep himself to himself; then there was the usual mix of people: some who will talk, some that won't.

There was a Scotsman in the other bed next to mine. He was cheerful and always reading the racing pages of the newspaper. He asked me if I backed the horses. I said I didn't, so that left us nothing to talk about.

There were a couple on the other side of the ward, one who was deaf, the other too sick to talk, so I thought it best not to bother with them. I tried my luck with the quiet bloke next to me. I told him my name and then a few jokes to break the ice. He smiled so I told him a few more but he never spoke back. I tried to get him to speak but he never bothered so I just lay there after that reading the papers and having the odd word with the Scotsman about anything.

I was on the drip a few days so I couldn't get out of bed; it seemed that the quiet man couldn't get out of bed either. I tried and tried to get him to talk but there was no way he would. I told him all my best jokes and even though he laughed he just wouldn't speak.

Then came the day that I was able to get out of bed and go for a wash. I was taken off the drip and I could once again move about. I got in my wheelchair and went to the bathroom for a wash.

When I got back to my bed a little later, and feeling much fresher from my wash, I went over to the quiet man's bed to ask him if there was anything that I could get him. He just shook his head.

I asked him what the thing over his legs was for. He turned over in his bed to face away from me. There was nothing I could do or say to make him look at me after that.

Later that day I asked one of the nurses about him. She told me that he had had his legs amputated some time ago and that he was having problems. I was totally gutted; there I was - the "Cheerful Charlie", all because I was feeling better and there this man was - so down in the dumps. I had another go at him.

'This your wheelchair?' I asked him. Not a word from him. He just lay there looking up at the ceiling. I tried again, this time with the old charm.

'Can you do wheelies in it?' The man was in his sixties and he didn't look the type who went around doing wheelies but I got his attention for a second even if he was looking at me as if I was simple.

'Watch I'll show you.' With that I did a few wheelies in front of him. He smiled at me. I was getting through.

'What's your name?' I asked him. He just looked at me; still no answer, so I looked at the bottom of his bed at the chart. There it was: Robert.

'Oh, Robert. Your name is Robert. Well I'm called Gary, Gaz for short.'

I smiled at him then left it up to him to speak if he wanted to. He just turned over to look the other way.

Syl and the lads visited and told me how nice it was to see me up and about in my chair again.

Syl told me, several times, not to play any jokes on anybody on the ward as I usually did and to keep out of trouble. I told her about Robert in the next bed. She, like me, felt so very sorry for him. We had a good chat and I told her that all was going well and I would be home in a couple of days.

The very next day the doctor came round and told me that I could go home, as everything was fine. I asked him what had been wrong. He said it was housemaid's knee, a thing called Bursitis. He also told me that it was caused by me crawling and not to be doing it as it would set it all off again.

I phoned Syl to tell her that I could come home. She said she would be there as soon as she could with my clothes.

As I was getting my things together the nurses were getting Robert out of his bed and putting him in his wheelchair. He looked over at me, so I wheeled myself over to say my goodbyes to him.

'Right Robert. I'm going home soon. I hope all goes well for you,' I said. He was going to have a bath; the nurses were getting his things ready for him.

He looked up at me and spoke. 'Bob! They call me, "Bob-in-the-bath". Ha ha!'

And those were the only words that he spoke to me. I sat there for a few minutes just smiling to myself. What a brave, fantastic man he was.

Syl arrived with Tony, who was driving the car, to take me home. We got all my things together, I said my goodbyes to the staff, then we headed for home.

Robert is someone I'll never forget. With just those few words he made me feel so good inside.

When we got home Syl attempted to make me use the wheelchair in the house but I would only use it in the kitchen. I got into my old routine very quickly; I did my exercises but only the ones on my back. Syl would watch me like a hawk to see that I didn't crawl or kneel on my bad knee.

Maureen, the physio-terrorist came to show me some exercises that I could do in my wheelchair. I would start by putting my arms down by the side of the chair, then slowly bending to my right to touch the middle of the wheel. Then do the same on the left. I was to do ten on each side but I did fifty.

Then I had to put my hands on my shoulders and turn around as far as I could to the right; then to the left, keeping my back as straight as I could. I was to do ten turnings on each side. Once again I did fifty. When I put all my exercises together I was kept busy all day because I would do them several times a day. This really kept me going. I was still moving about on my Zimmer frame as well so I really was fit.

1988 was coming to a close and my MS, though not getting better, seemed to be slowing down. I had lost a lot in such a short space of time I didn't know what it was going to take from me next, or when I was going to go through an emotional minefield that I kept to myself.

My right leg now didn't work at all; one minute my bladder emptied, the next it wouldn't. I couldn't take the chance of not wearing a leg-bag when shopping, as I had often done in the past, now everything was going haywire, though I could in the house as I had the clamp.

My arms were very strong and I did not fatigue, however much I exercised. I had built myself up to a good level of fitness. In fact my stamina was great. I had no problem with my hands, as I had before; I was doing the exercises that I had made up on my fingers all the time.

I would touch my thumb to my little finger, then the next, and the next, then the next. I built up speed each day. Then I used both hands at the same time. This was hard at first but I got there. It really is a great exercise for the hands and helps them become well coordinated; and it keeps them supple.

I was able to get about again, thanks to the wheelchair. I once said that I would never use it in the house, just outside. But then I had to start using it from the car to the kitchen door as my legs got worse. Now I was going to have to use it in the kitchen as well.

This really hurt me inside. On the outside I was full of it, always telling jokes and smiling but on the inside I was so low and getting lower with every passing day.

I wanted for nothing and my family made my life wonderful. I had all the love I could wish for but the things that I wanted to do were now getting too hard.

I wasn't walking on my Zimmer frame any more. It was more like my arms were holding me up and I just dragged myself along. This was hurting me physically but I just couldn't, and wouldn't, stop doing it because it was the only way that I had of staying on my feet.

I was even finding it hard to get out of the chair that I sat on in the living room. I now had to fall to my knees then crawl to the stairs just so as I could pull myself up by the banister. I would crawl into the kitchen and pull myself up at the sink. I was now having to use my arms more and more and my legs less and less.

I was able to stand, some days, using the wall to balance, or my Zimmer frame. But then on other days I could only get about if I used my wheelchair or by crawling, which was so hard to do and even harder to accept.

I never knew from one day to the next how I would be, so I took every day as it came and worked around it, adapting the different days to the moods of the MS, never letting it beat me. That one thing I promised myself from day one.

I got my eyesight sorted out. I went to the opticians and had it tested. There was nothing wrong with my right eye but the left was scarred from the MS. I had glasses made and they were fine, I could see out of both eyes again. It was so nice to get something back for once instead of losing it slowly all the time.

All in all, 1988 had seen me accepting things more. I had come to terms with my wheelchair; I had accepted that I needed help getting in and out of the bath; I'd had hand rails put in the toilet and now I was even going to have a stairlift installed. This would give me back that little piece of independence I so longed for.

It was Halloween and the kids from the neighborhood had been knocking on the front door trick-or-treating most of the night.

Syl would answer the door and say to the little kids, 'Oh! Some kids have just been and I gave them everything that I had, sorry,' when really she hadn't but this was the sort of thing she did all the time. This particular night the doorbell rang and I went to look out of the curtains.

'Leave it, it's only kids,' Syl said. So we left it; then again, Ding-Dong. 'Leave it, they will go soon, just ignore them.'

'It could be someone else,' I said thinking it could well have been.

'No, it's kids; so like I say, leave it.' So we left it and carried on watching the TV.

Then, Ding-Dong, Ding-Dong, and Ding-Dong, Ding-Dong, on and on it went until I said, 'Answer the front door, Syl.'

'No, I'll look through the window first,' she said all flustered, as she sneakily peeped through a little gap she had just made in the curtain.

'Who is it, Syl can you see anything?'

She turned to me and went, 'Shush! It's a bloke with some kids walking away.'

I wouldn't mind but the television was on and they could easily have heard it outside, so why bother to whisper.

'See, I told you it was just kids.'

Just then the bell went again, Ding-Dong, Ding-Dong.

'I'll go, Syl you sit there,' I said.

'No!' With that Syl jumped up and went to the door. I could hear familiar voices. The living room door opened and in walked my mate, Dave Peploe, from Wythenshawe.

'Hello, Gaz, how are you?' he asked. 'I've been ringing your doorbell, and knocking, for about half an hour now.'

I started laughing. 'Syl thought that it was kids trick-or-treating,' I told him. 'That's why she wouldn't open the door.'

Dave watched me trying to get up from my chair. It had been a long time since I had seen him; he had never seen me on my Zimmer frame and he was really taken aback.

He had come down with a few of my old friends from Wythenshawe to take me for a pint. It took me about half an hour to get ready and in that time Syl had told them how I was and how we had been coping over the years.

We went to the local pub and had a chat about darts and how things used to be. I even used my wheelchair, as there was no other way that I could have gone out. The lads had no idea just how bad I really was now, as I hadn't told them anything about my illness and I put on one hell of a show for them to hide it.

We talked about everything except MS. I cracked a few jokes about myself not being able to play darts anymore. I said that I had to put the darts in my mouth, now, and someone then threw the board at me. We had a very good night; it was so good to see my old friends again. I got in that night and I had so much gossip to tell Syl about where we used to live. I found myself wishing I was living back down there with them again. It was one of the last times that I saw my old mates; the only other times were at friends' funerals.

Times change and so do people; they each go their own ways in life. My mates had all played a great part in my life - parts in my life that I will cherish all my days - and I was glad to be a part of theirs.

One night the lads were talking to me and Syl, and Adam asked us why it was that I walked in his dreams but not when he was awake. I just held him as tight as I could and said that dreams could come true someday. Someday!

That night I cried an ocean of tears over what Adam had said. It really hurt and hit home. I can take the pain and the different things that were happening to my body through the MS but this was a different kind of hurting. This went deep into my soul.

As if I wasn't determined enough before this, I was now even more determined to get myself back on my feet. I would do it now no matter what the consequences were. The only problem, though, was the spirit was willing and my upper-body was willing, but my legs didn't get the message. It seems like it never rains unless it pours on me sometimes.

As always, something happened to me to take the edge off what I was doing. This time I got toothache and needed to go to the dentist's. So off I went to see him. I forgot that his surgery was up a flight of stairs. It took ages for Syl and me to climb, one at a time, on my bum but we did it, as usual, and I got my tooth fixed.

I had never thought about things like the dentist's or even the barber's. It was the same sort of thing there, only this time I was finding it hard to get in the chair to get my hair cut. In the end I started to let Syl's mobile hairdresser cut my hair. It's the things you take for granted that you overlook the most.

At night I was finding it difficult to sleep. I had a sort of cramp in my right leg. I would no sooner get in bed than the cramp would start and the pain was terrible. I had to get out of bed and try to walk it off. The only problem was I couldn't walk so I crawled round the bedroom and did some exercises on it; most of the time this would ease the pain a little.

I asked Maureen, the physio-terrorist, what could be causing it. She thought that I was overdoing it with my exercising. She was right, so I didn't do any exercises on it for a week and it was wonderful. I was becoming my own worst enemy by trying to do too much all at once on my legs. I decided to do only light exercises on my legs from then on, just enough to loosen them and to make me feel as though I wasn't giving in.

Christmas was on us and I found myself looking round the shops again for presents. It was fine shopping for family and friends, we did it together, but to buy for Syl was a problem - no not a problem, more a nightmare! She was always with me. I could never get away from her for long enough to buy her present. I had to ask family to shop for me without her knowing but she somehow always found out.

It was just before Christmas. I was feeling fine all day, all the shopping for presents had been done now. We only had the food shopping to do. I was watching TV and relaxing. I'd been having problems passing urine all that day and I starting to feel quite ill. I started to shiver and my teeth chattered, but I was sweating and my body was hot. I went to bed.

Syl brought me a cup of coffee and a couple of painkillers as she thought that I had flu, but within an hour I became worse. Syl phoned for the doctor who, when he came, said that I had a water infection. I was given antibiotics and told to drink plenty of fluid to help flush it out. This was now something else that I was going to have problems with over the years.

1989 Saw Maureen the physio-terrorist change my exercises. I was now doing a lot more stretching on my legs whilst I was on the floor and more exercises as I was in my wheelchair. I would put one hand on each wheel then push down, so as to lift my bottom off the seat of the wheelchair. This was a form of press-up to help my arms and it did. I was told to do ten but as usual I doubled that, and did them quite a few times each day.

There was also an exercise using my weights. I would have one in each hand down by the side of the wheels of my chair; I would slowly lift both arms at the same time till the weights met over my head, then slowly lower them to my side. I would do ten of these, also a few times a day.

Next I would start as before with the weights at my side, then slowly raise them out and up till they were level with my shoulders, hold for a count of five, then slowly lower them back to my side. Then I would get on my back on the floor with my knees up and slowly let them go to one side, with my arms stretching in the other direction. This is a great loosening and stretching exercise for hips, waist and thighs. I would also do my normal workout which I had cut down to just press-ups, sit-ups and back-work. I was doing the pelvic exercises three to four times a day to help me with my bladder problems, which had now taken a turn for the worse.

It was the same old problem: one minute I just could not stop running to the toilet, or should I say crawling; the next I was finding it very hard to go without pushing my stomach. I had been here before, having to do the same old things to relieve myself from the misery of this awful side of my MS, the side that I hated the most. I was drinking no coffee just lemon water and the occasional cup of tea. Often I drank lemon-barley water which, some days, really did the trick in helping me pass water; but no matter what I did I was still getting lots of bladder and kidney infections.

The lads also helped me to do some work on my legs. They helped me as often as they could. I would lie on the floor, flat on my stomach, then try to bring the heel of my foot to touch my bottom. I could just about do two with my left leg but none at all with my right, so the lads would help me from here on; they would move them for me.

They both did twenty on each leg, then more than likely we would end up playfully wrestling on the floor. Syl would do one exercise with me, too. I would still be flat on my stomach on the floor. She would bend my right leg up and hold it till I thought that I could hold it myself, then she'd let go. This took a lot of effort but the feeling that I got inside on the odd occasion that I managed to do it was wonderful.

We had just got Sky TV installed and American wrestling was the thing the lads wanted to watch the most. We would sit there in the living room as a family watching this crazy wrestling. I wasn't all that keen but to see the lads' faces when their hero came into the ring was fantastic, something not to be missed. Even Syl got carried away with it all - so much so that if you were sitting near her when she was watching it, you would have to duck, as most of the time she forgot herself and hit out trying to copy the moves. It always ended up with us wrestling the lads on the floor.

Towards the end of January, Maureen the physio terrorist thought that it would be best if I had a course of intense physiotherapy and the best place for that was the hospital.

Tameside hospital was just opening their new Physiotherapy Department, so she set about getting me an intense course there. Within a couple of weeks I had to go to see Martina, one of the physiotherapists. She would assess me and tell me just what I could and could not do and tell me what sort of treatment that I could look forward to getting.

So, Syl and I went to the hospital to meet Martina for the first time. She was very nice and showed us around the department. It was wonderful, full of the most fantastic things like parallel bars, just the sort of thing that I needed to help me to get on my feet and practice my walking. Then there were the electronically controlled beds which went up or down at the touch of a button; benches to do exercises on, not like at home where I just got on the hard floor. The floor there was smooth. There were no carpets so I would be able to move my feet much easier across it, if I got the chance; then there was the hydrotherapy pool with a hoist, a wonderful thing.

After looking around the department Martina asked me some questions about my MS. Things like, what I could and could not do, and what sort of exercises I was doing at home. Then she asked me to get onto one of the benches. I did some of the usual exercises I did at home. After doing them she asked me to stand up. I could only do this with the help of my hands and Syl holding on to me.

I got back into my wheelchair and went over to·where there were rubber mats on the floor. Martina asked if I could get out of my wheelchair and onto them, which I could, just about. I was on my back on the mats with my knees bent up. We did some knee rolling from side to side, then some stretching on my legs. Martina said that would be enough for that day and to get back into my wheelchair, which I did with the help of her and Mike, one of the male staff who did a lot of work with us.

I was given another appointment for early the following day, which was great as it meant that we could take the lads to school first and still be at the department for nine thirty.

On the way home from the first session of physiotherapy I felt fantastic and so excited that, now, I was going to be able to fight back, with the help of all that equipment. This was something that Maureen, the physio-terrorist, and I didn't have the luxury of when we did the exercises at home.

That night all I could talk about was that fantastic gym and all the different equipment, which I might get the chance to use. Plus there was the hydrotherapy pool, I was really hoping that I would get the chance to use that.

The following day I was up very early to have a bath and get ready for physiotherapy. We dropped the lads off at school then went straight to the hospital. The parking there was terrible, there weren't that many spaces, so Mike told me that it would be OK to park at the back of the department, which I did.

We got in the gym and started working right away. I got on one of the beds this time. It was wonderful, so easy to get onto and so comfortable to do exercises on. We started with some loosening work, then we did some strengthening work on my back. I was asked to swing my legs over the side of the bed so my feet were on the floor, then I was asked to try and stand without using my hands.

This I just couldn't do as the bed was too low, so they started to raise it using the controls. As it elevated, easily, my feet stayed on the floor while the rest of my body was being raised. I got to an almost standing position but there was still enough left for me to do to get to stand up properly.

I was asked if I could stand up fully without using my hands this time but it was still very difficult. I was trying to throw myself up with a jerk and a wiggle, not using my hips or bottom, as I should have been doing. I was told to sit back down again whilst the bed was lowered to the original height. I then returned to lying flat on the bed with my knees bent and was told to lift my bottom off the bed. Now this was very, very difficult for me to do but I did it, just. We spent a lot of time doing this exercise until it was time to go. I was told to do no more exercises for the rest of that day and for once I did what I was told. I just caught up on other things that needed to be done around the house. I was feeling so great after the workout I had just done I felt as though I was going to finally get somewhere at long last.

Tony had been asking me to go and look round some fishing tackle shops with him, as he wanted to take up fishing as a hobby, so we went out later that day to look at some tackle shops and some waters that I would be able to fish. This wasn't easy, to find waters I could get to fish from my wheelchair. We did find a few places, though, and thought we could give them a try.

Tony had bought some tackle for his own use from the tackle shop and I had my old tackle, as I used to be a very keen fisherman. I'd given it up years ago when I first got MS. It was nice to return to a hobby that I once loved to do, now that Tony wanted me to go fishing with him and teach him how to fish.

For the rest of the week I went to physiotherapy every day. I was loving it. I was feeling so good inside. I thought that I was finally getting somewhere with my standing, thanks to the height-adjustable bed and all the floor exercises I was doing to strengthen my legs and back. And now, besides all the physiotherapy, I was going to get out and about with Tony now, taking up fishing.

It really helps when you feel good inside and I was feeling very, very good. I knew that I was on the up for once. Things were going well!

Over the weekend Tony and I decided to do a spot of fishing on the local canal in Ashton. We had heard from a couple of friends in the pub that it was good there, so off we went. The weather was very cold but that didn't matter. What mattered was getting out there on the canal and fishing. I was in my wheelchair at the side of the canal, Tony was about five feet away from me sitting in a garden chair. We were well prepared. We had flasks of hot drinks and loads and loads of food. It was more like a safari expedition than a day out fishing.

I showed Tony how to set up his rod and tackle and he did well. We were there for a good hour before the first fish was caught. Tony was well chuffed, it was the first fish that he had ever caught, a little perch. It was flapping all over the bank, dangling from the end of his rod.

He shouted over to me, 'Gaz! Gaz! What should I do with this?'

Like I say, dangling from the end of his rod was this little fish, the size of a sardine. 'Take the hook out,' I told him.

'How?' he asked in a puzzled sort of way.

'Pick it up and take it out of its mouth,' I said.

With that he went to pick it up and it wriggled.

'Woo!' he screamed, jumping back.

'Don't be a tart, Tony, pick it up. It won't bite you,' I shouted.

'No it's one of them with the stinging things on its back. A... A... Perch!' Tony yelled back.

Now me and some of the lads in the pub had told Tony not to touch a perch; they needed expert handling as they had fins on their backs that could sting you very badly and cause all kinds of pain and discomfort.

'Tony, bring it here,' I shouted.

Tony, by now, had ran a good thirty yards down the bank with this fish dangling from his line. He stopped, turned around, and walked back to me. I took hold of the fish and tried to get the hook out of its mouth.

'The hook is stuck, Tony. Pass me the disgorger.'

He started to look round the tackle box. 'We ain't got one, will these pliers do?'

He had these huge pair of household pliers, the sort you use on jobs around the house or on the car.

'It's only a little fish, Tony, not Moby Dick. I'll sort it out without them.'

I sorted his fish out for him, then carried on with my fishing till Tony shouted, 'Gaz!'

'What?'

'Want a drink of coffee and a cig?' he said, smiling at me like a Cheshire cat.

'Go on then, you've twisted my arm.'

He walked over to me, brought me a cup of coffee and a cigarette, and crouched down besides my wheelchair.

'Good this ain't it, Gaz. A bit cold, like, but OK.'

'Yes, it's a lot better on a summer's day though,' I replied.

'I want to catch bigger fish than that little thing, something like carp,' he said.

I could see his little brain ticking away, then!

'We could even go sea fishing when the weather gets better. What do you think?' he chuckled to me.

Just then my float went under. The fish was putting up a good fight. I was so relieved when I reeled it in to find a good-sized perch on the end.

'Here you go, Tony. I will hold it while you take the hook out,' I said to him.

'Is it one of them perch things?' he cautiously asked.

'Yes,' I said.

'Then you'd better do it,' he said, backing away from the fish.

'Tony, it was a joke mate! We were winding you up the other night in the pub. They're safe.'

'You lying *******!' he said. 'I've got a good mind to throw you in for that, you lying wart. But then I would have to fish you out afterwards.'

Tony took the hook out of the fish's mouth and we carried on fishing for the rest of the day in spite of all the jokes. Happy days.

Chapter Eight

Monday couldn't come quick enough for me. I had just had a great weekend relaxing and fishing. Now I was ready and refreshed and looking forward to doing my physiotherapy in the gym. We arrived bright and early at the department. Martina and Mike were already waiting for me. We went straight into the gym; I got on one of the benches and started to do my loosening up exercises. I then did my rolling and stretching exercises on the floor, with Mike, as usual, watching every move that I made.

It wasn't just doing exercises, it was a good laugh as well. We did plenty of work, believe me, but we told jokes as we were doing it. It was just great fun. I was enjoying every minute of it. There was no way that I could overdo the amount of exercises I was supposed to do. Martina and Mike made sure of that. There was no way that I could have done similar exercises at home; I didn't have the equipment to do it for one, or I would have made no mistake in doing them!

This was the second week of my treatment and I could really feel a difference in myself. I had a lot more strength in my back and hips because I was able to exercises them better using the benches and mats. My sitting up was much stronger. I wasn't falling from side to side as much as I had been, so all in all I could feel a huge difference in myself. There was still a lot of work to be done and a long way still to go to reach where I wanted to be.

Every time I went for my treatment I would ask Martina or Mike if I could use the parallel bars; every time they gave the same answer: "Not today! You're not ready for them yet!"

All that week we did the stretching and strengthening exer-

86

cises then on the Friday we went into the wax room. This was the room where they treated people with sprains, or those who'd just had their plaster cast off and needed further treatment, that sort of thing. The electronically-controlled bed that I used to help me into a standing position was also there. I was asked to get on the bed so I could do some more back-work then practice my standing.

The bed was raised after I'd done a few exercises on my back and I was asked to stand up the rest of the way. I was almost there! I didn't wriggle or use my hands. I just used my back, as I should have done. There was just a little more to do on this now but not bad after only a fortnight's work.

I was so pleased I just couldn't explain to you how I felt. It was just so good; everybody in the room was pleased with what we had achieved. Everything was coming together, all the hard work on my back was now paying dividends in a big, big way. I think it's a combination of the equipment you use and the expertise of the staff that does it, plus a hell of a lot of graft from yourself.

You feel that you have accomplished something after working-out in the gym, whereas at home when I did the exercises on the kitchen floor it wasn't the same. Even when Syl or the lads did them with me, I just didn't get the same effect.

It's just a pity that Maureen the physio-terrorist didn't have all this equipment. If she did she would have to carry it around in something like the size of a mobile library van. Mind you that's not a bad idea, a big van with writing on the side: Maureen, the Phyio-terrorist's Mobile Gym.

Over the next month I improved greatly in the things that I was able to do, though my walking was still something to be desired. My back was much stronger and I was now standing a lot straighter when I used my Zimmer frame. My legs were so much stronger. They were now supporting me rather than my arms, which had been the case when I first started at the department.

The things I had achieved were fantastic: I was bridging my back up off the bed, I was able to stand without using my arms; OK I was still using the electronic bed to get me to a certain height but that height was a lot lower now. In fact, I was almost down to the normal sitting position of a chair, so all in all I was over the moon with the progress that I had made in such a short space of time. And the beauty of it all was that I was doing it, not the steroids! It was easier for me to do my exercises knowing that with everything I was doing I was getting stronger.

Each day I would ask when I could go in the hydrotherapy pool to do some exercises; I got the same answer as I did over the parallel bars: "Not yet!"

One morning I turned up and Martina was in the hydrotherapy pool, helping to treat some patients. Mike was going to do my workout with me while she was busy. We went through my exercises and when it was time to go I told Mike I'd just pop in to say goodbye to Martina. I did this and took the opportunity to have a good look at what the other patients were doing. Well, what I saw looked great. Some of the patients were walking round the pool holding on to the side doing exercises.

God! I wanted to join them right then and there. This sort of thing was the thing for me! Oh, yes. I could just see myself in that pool doing a workout, but best of all would be the feeling of walking again as the water would be supporting me instead of the Zimmer frame.

This was now my chance to ask Jill, who was the physiotherapist in charge of the pool. Martina walked up to me and I asked her if there was a chance I could have a go in the pool on my next visit to the department. She was worried that I might fatigue in the water as it was very warm. I said that I did not fatigue easily, as she knew from working with me, and I would only stay in the water for as long as she thought fit. She had a word with Jill and they both agreed to let me have a go on my next visit.

This was all that I wanted, the chance to show them that I could do it and that I would be OK once I was in there. I was told to bring some shorts or swimming trunks the next morning. When Syl and I left the department we went straight to the market to buy some.

I was so excited at the thought of going into the pool I couldn't wait for morning to come. I was like a big kid. This was going to be my chance to maybe walk again.

Next morning I was up bright and early, washed and ready for the day ahead. I even put on my shorts to save time getting ready. I was just like a kid again - I used to put my swimming trunks on under my clothes so that I was ready to get straight in the water when I went swimming with school. I was as excited now as I was then.

We got to the Physiotherapy Department, Martina was waiting for me in the hydrotherapy room. I got undressed as quickly as I could, then got into my wheelchair and went out to the poolside where they were waiting for me. I had to put on some floats, even though I was a good swimmer. By the time I had put on all the floats they wanted me to, I looked like someone out of one of those sea disaster movies, but if that's what it was going to take to get me in the water, I would wear them. I would have even used a raft if they told me I had to.

They told me about the hoist and how I was to get onto it. The hoist was lowered to the side of the pool where I was in my wheelchair. I then had to get out of my wheelchair and onto the hoist, which was just like a bed, then lie flat on it. A strap was put around me for safety reasons. I was then lifted a few feet and lowered into the water where Martina was waiting for me.

The hoist was stopped just as it touched the water and the strap was undone. Martina helped me out and I could feel my feet touch the bottom of the pool. Oh yes! I was in! The water was lovely and warm, not like the freezing cold water you sometimes get in some swimming baths. I was led to the side of the pool by Martina and told to just get used to the water for a minute. She kept asking me if I was OK. Well I was. I had this great sensation, the sensation of standing up all by myself.

We then started to do some work. She asked me to lift up my right leg, which I did manage to get off the floor just a touch. Then she asked me to do the same with my left leg. Now this one was much easier to do. I got it to move without any trouble. There I was in the pool standing on one leg. I must have looked like one of those flamingos.

Martina moved a couple of feet away from me and asked me to walk to her, so I slowly moved towards her. My legs were moving! I was walking on my own. No Zimmer frame, no one holding my arms, no walking-stick, just me by myself unaided. I said to Syl, who was watching at the side of the pool, 'Look, Syl no hands!'

What a feeling to be walking freely again even if it was only a few steps. I did it again, this time holding Martina's hand and we went a good few more steps. OK I had floats on and I had hold of Martina's hands, but my legs were holding me up and they were moving.

This was something that I had not done in years - walk

unaided, and to have that feeling again was magic. I could feel my throat tightening I was feeling so emotional.

I did a few more things then this alarm clock at the side of the pool went off to tell me my time was up. I got back into the hoist and was lifted out of the water and helped into my wheelchair. I was given a bathrobe to put on then went back to the changing rooms. I had a nice hot drink and lay on the bed for a few moments, drinking and relishing what I had just done for a moment before I got dressed. When I got back to the side of the pool Martina asked me if I was OK. I was, I was feeling better than ever.

Well, I had done the thing I wanted to do. I had been into the pool and it was everything I thought it would have been, and more. Now I was hoping that I would be allowed to go in more often and to walk once again unaided. But that was not to be.

I was allowed to go into the pool a couple of times more over the next few weeks then it was thought that it would be better for me if I did not go into the water as I, "might fatigue".

It wasn't Martina's decision to stop me as she, like me, thought that I was doing well. I never found out whose decision it was but it really, really hurt me to have this one thing taken away. I was doing so well and feeling like I had never felt in years, but that didn't matter to whoever made this "brainstorming" decision. It was thought that I, "might fatigue", and that was that.

What a load of twaddle! If I was going to fatigue I would have done it before now. No one asked me how I felt, just: "No. That's it. No more.".

This took me some time to get over, I was so deeply hurt inside. I was really doing well in the pool but now I had no choice but to go on with the gym-work as before. I loved doing that anyway but now I'd had something that had given me hope taken away from me without even an explanation. Whoever had had the idea to stop me going into the pool didn't know me personally. They didn't know what I was able to do. All they knew was I had MS and people with MS "fatigue", so that was it.

I worked harder and harder in the gym, hoping that one day whoever made the decision to keep me out of the pool would see that I really was fit, didn't "fatigue" that easily and let me have the chance of going back in the pool.

We got to April and the men had come to measure the stairs

for the stairlift. We were told that it might only take a couple of weeks before it was fitted. I was doing well getting down the stairs and it was a good sort of exercising; dangerous, but an exercise none the less.

Going up was still a major problem, though, so the sooner the better for the stairlift being fitted. Then I would have more of the independence that I wanted.

I was doing very well with my gym-work. Martina and Mike started me on the parallel bars which was very hard to do as I was having to put one foot in front of the other without throwing my right hip out, as I used to. But I managed it. I did slip up on the odd occasion but beady-eyed Mike or Martina were there to make me put it right.

I would get out of my wheelchair at one end of the bars then walk to the other, turn around and walk back and sit down in my wheelchair again. I would do this several times when I was in the gym until the day that Mike asked to see how far I could walk on a Zimmer frame.

A Zimmer frame was put in front of my wheelchair so I would be able to walk straight away when I got to my feet. Mike walked at the side of me while Syl followed just behind me with the wheelchair so I could sit down if I needed to. I set off from the wax room, walked right through the waiting room then out into the main corridor and down to the lifts where it was time for me to sit down. I wasn't tired just totally shocked at what I had done! I just had to sit down. Mike was raving and jumping up on the spot, he was so pleased at the distance I'd just managed to walk. Syl gave me a big kiss and had a tear in her eye that said it all. I had just achieved the thing that I had worked so hard for, I had walked again.

We went back into the gym and everyone was so pleased when Mike told them all how far I had just walked. This was fantastic, the progress that I had made in such a short time. I was so thankful to everyone. I was able to get about the house a lot better, too. I wasn't using the wheelchair in the house at all now. I wasn't crawling, I was using the Zimmer frame all the time and life was looking a lot better.

The next month saw the stairlift installed. The fitters came at about eight o'clock and it was done the same morning. The first time I used it was to show the workmen that everything was fine.

When they left it was up to me to use it whenever I needed.

Well, I used it to go up the stairs loads of times but I always walked down them so I would have to use my legs. This was fine at first then a problem arose. Whenever anyone came to the front door as I was using the lift I would panic. I just didn't like to be seen on it by strangers. It was OK family seeing me using it but I felt as though I was on display if anyone else saw me.

This caused problems in the house but only of my own making, and it took a long time to come to terms with them. Problems like: if the lads' friends came round to play on the computer I wouldn't use the lift until they were in the bedroom, even if I was bursting to go to the toilet. I know it sounds stupid but it was something that I found difficult to come to terms with.

I did finally but it took such a long time. The fact was that I saw it as being beaten every time I used it and I didn't want people to think that I was a loser, as I'm not and that's not the sort of image I wanted to give them.

I was fine when family and friends came, they even had a go on it for themselves, especially the children. They loved to try it out. To them it was a ride up the stairs, a big wonderful way to get to the top, and I always made a fuss of them on it, so that it would not be strange to them.

At the Physiotherapy Unit they were having raffles for various things and to raise money for the baby unit. We were talking about it at home when Syl's sister, Beryl came round to the house for a chat. She told us she had heard about a marathon, a wheelchair marathon run around the industrial estate at Stretford. I asked her to get me the details about it so that I could enter.

She got them back for us within a couple of days. I read them and thought that I would enter to raise money for the hospital. I asked our Tony if he would run around the course with me so that we would raise even more money. He said it was no problem and that he would even push me round if I wanted him to. Well, I didn't like to tell him but that was what he was going to do anyway!

We sent the form off and went into training - we went to the pub twice, sometimes three times, a week and Tony would "train" at the side of me as we went. Phew!

Now, Tony was a self-employed plasterer in the building trade and not what you could call the athletic type. In fact, the only athletic thing about Tony was his nose: it kept running.

We told everyone at the hospital what we were doing and we started to get lots of sponsors. Now all we needed to do was the marathon. (Easy peasy!)

It was the Sunday of the marathon and Tony and Jane rolled up to our house as arranged, but just, and I mean just! His car had packed up as he reached our back gate. He spent some time trying to fix it but had to stop as it would have taken too long and we wouldn't have got to the marathon on time. Instead he went in my sister Maureen's little Mini with Jane and my mum.

They were coming with us to cheer us on and enjoy the day. I had Syl and the lads in our car, plus bags and things out of Tony's car.

We all set off in great spirits. Tony and I were really looking forward to doing it. It took us about half an hour to get to Kellogg's, where the race was being held. We parked the cars, got all that we needed out of them, then went to give our names in to the race organisers.

This was the eighth "Open Trafford Wheelchair Marathon", hosted by Kellogg's at their site in Stretford. They put on the most fantastic day for everyone. Syl, the lads, my mum, our Moie and Jane had made themselves very comfy in a corner of the café, where all the drinks were free.

Tony and I were looking round the place when I told Tony that I needed to go to the toilet. We went to the disabled toilet but there was already someone using it. All the other toilets were in use or had people waiting to use them and there was no way that I could have stood up to use the urinals.

Tony remembered that there were some more toilets just over the other side of the canteen so we went to them. It was a bit of a struggle to get the wheelchair through the door but we managed to cope with it OK.

There were three toilet cubicles in there along with the same amount of urinals. Well, like I said there was no way that I could use the urinals as I didn't have my frame to hold me up, so I had to use one of the cubicles. They were the sort whose doors have a gap at the top and the bottom, those really flimsy ones.

Tony held my wheelchair while I made my way into the toilet. I was holding on to the top of the cubicle so that I could walk in and sit down, as there was no other way that I could have stayed on my feet and sorted myself out toilet-wise.

I closed the door behind me then went about my business. After I had finished I tried to stand back up. Oops. I fell!

The toilet was too low for me to get back up on my feet and I fell to my knees, so I shouted. 'Tony!'

'What?' he said.

'You're not going to believe this, mate!' I shouted

'I am! What?' he tutted.

'I've fallen and I can't get back up.'

'I knew it! I knew it! You and ****** toilets. Move from the door,' he yelled.

'I can't! I'm right behind it,' I told him.

Well, he was ranting and raving all over the place. He really was getting his little self in a bit of a paddy. 'Trust you! I knew it! I knew it! You and ****** toilets.'

'Calm down, Tony! Calm down!' I tried to tell him but he really was losing it by this time.

'Calm down! How the **** can I with you!'

'Look, Tony, my legs are in the next cubicle,' I tried to explain.

'Oh! How the **** have you done that?'

Now, when I fell my legs somehow just slipped under the gap at the bottom of the cubicle into the toilet next door and there was a bar that was stopping me from moving them myself, as I had fallen very awkwardly. By this time Tony was losing it in a big, and I mean big, way.

'Tony. You will have to go in the toilet next door and push my legs through for me,' I said to him.

He went into the cubicle where my legs were, then he started.

'How have you done this?' he shouted to me. '******* ballet dancing!'

'I don't know, just push them back through.'

With that he mumbled something

and pushed my legs back into the toilet with me. God! I was so relieved. 'Nice one, Tony,' I said.

'Right! Open the door now,' he shouted. I knelt up, unbolted the door and opened it to reveal a very, very red-faced Tony.

'OK, Tony, me mate!' I said, smiling.

'OK! OK! Just get back in your wheelchair,' he said.

He was not a happy bunny by this time.

'You're going to have to give me a hand, my legs have gone dead.'

Well, his face was a picture when I said this.

'Right! What do you want me to do?'

'Put the wheelchair in front of me and I'll pull myself into it.'

With that he put the wheelchair right in front of me and I tried to pull myself up so I could get into it. I then realised that my shorts were only half-way up, so I looked at Tony, smiled, and said, 'Tony?'

'What now?' he growled, as he stared at me.

'Give us a hand to pull my shorts up, mate.'

'Do you know I hate you, I really do.'

He came into the cubicle and stood behind me while I was kneeling and holding on to my wheelchair. He'd just started to pull up my shorts when the door opened. Both our heads turned sharply to face the door where a man, with a very strange sort of look on his face, was standing.

We all looked at each other, shook our heads, then the man did a quick about-turn and left, with Tony shouting after him, 'It's OK! He's my brother-in-law!' at the top of his voice.

He threw me into my wheelchair and pushed me back, at some speed, to where the rest of the family was sitting.

'I will never go in another toilet with you. Ever!' Tony said to me.

'You don't mean that, Tony,' I said, laughing.

'Oh, yes I do. Now let's go and do this marathon.'

With that we made our way outside to where they were lining up to start the race.

There were some fantastic wheelchairs there, some really sporty ones that were there to race. Not like Tony and me who were there just to raise money for the hospital and have a lot of fun on the way round.

All the wheelchairs were lining up. I kissed Syl and the family, Tony kissed Jane, then we made our way to the front among all kinds of wheelchairs. There were electric ones, scooters, racing ones, so many different types and so many different people, people from all walks of life.

There were parents pushing their children, there were children pushing their parents, there were friends pushing friends, there was this terrific atmosphere. Tony and I were so excited about it we got right to the front. The tension was really building up.

Tony said we would get away quick and have a go at a fast time. I just looked at him as if he was simple but he meant it. He wanted to have a go at a fast time. There was just no way that we could do a fast time, we weren't that fit and the wheelchair that I was in weighed a ton, so there was no chance. Or was there?

All the racing wheelchairs went in front and set off a couple of minutes before us. Then it was our turn. Tony grabbed the handles of the wheelchair, I had my hands ready on the wheels. The man who was starting the race lifted an arm and fired the starting pistol. Bang!

We were off. Tony flew down the road like a bat out of hell. His little legs were going twenty to the dozen, so were my arms. Then there was a problem, my feet fell off the footrests and under the wheelchair. I stopped wheeling and pulled them back on, while Tony carried on pushing. Our Gary was running just behind us. He wanted to do the marathon with us but as soon as we saw him we shouted to him to go back which, luckily, he did.

We had gone about a quarter of a mile when we had to stop to get a token to prove that we had passed that checkpoint. Then we carried on at a more leisurely pace. We could see lots of wheelchairs behind us and a few making their way to where we were. A lot of wheelchairs passed us but we didn't care, we were doing our own thing and that was all that mattered.

We kept stopping for a chat and a cigarette, then we did a load of wheeling and pushing. Tony could stand on the back of the wheelchair and I would wheel us using my arms. It was great, we were having a ball. Then we saw a racing wheelchair going past us.

Tony looked at me and said, 'We've been lapped.'

That was it! We put a spurt on and really went at a pace. We could see Kellogg's and crowds of people lining each side of the road, cheering as the wheelchairs went past.

Wow! Now we really put a lot of effort into it. As we were going through the crowds we wanted to look the part, and boy did we. We got a second wind as we were passing through the people. They were cheering us on. It was fantastic, we loved every minute of it - that feeling was wonderful.

When we got out of sight of the crowds we stopped. Tony sat on the grass fighting for his breath. So was I, we had put so much into it. We looked at each other and smiled a smug smile of satisfaction.

We were sat there for a while. I was slumped in my wheelchair having a cigarette and talking to Tony when some people passed us. I shouted to them as they were passing, 'Chins up! Only one lap to go now.'

They looked at us as if we were daft and said, 'No lads. Two!'

Tony and me looked at each other and said at the same time, 'Two? Two!' We started to run again, first at a fast pace then more of a "run, stop, and fight for breath" sort of pace which then went into a gentle sort of trot, well, walk!

It seemed to take us forever to finish the second lap with all the stops we made for cigarette breaks and whatnots but we did it, but only just.

Then it was the third and final lap. We said that we would give it all we had which, for Tony and me at that stage, was not a lot. The weather was hot, very hot, a lovely day for sunbathing but not for running a marathon.

We kept stopping at the stages along the route for drinks and at one of the stop points I threw a couple of cups of water over myself to help me to cool down. When we got to the next stop point, Tony did no more than pick the bucket up off the floor and went to pour it over his head. The Boy Scouts, who were handing out the drinks, shouted for him to stop. It was too late. He poured the full bucket over his head except this time it wasn't water, it was an orange cordial they had just mixed.

Well! His hair stood on end just like one of those seventies punk-rockers. He looked as though he had just been Tangoed. The poor Boy Scouts didn't know what to do. They just looked at him in total disbelief. I could see them trying to hold back from laughing out loud but me, well. I just let rip. The tears were running down my face. I couldn't stop laughing at him. What a wazzock he looked.

That was it. Tony grabbed the handles of the wheelchair and pushed me down the road shouting, 'Not a word! Not a ******* word.'

We stopped a bit further down the road and we ended up laughing about it then, all the way to the finish line.

What a sight to see. Those wonderful, last few yards. Everyone there cheered us and there were plenty of people at the finish line. What a feeling. We had done it! Fourteen miles done in just under two hours. Not bad for two out of condition blokes.

We got our medals - I gave mine to Syl. I told her that she needed a medal to put up with me. Tony gave his to Jane, then we all made our way to the canteen where Kellogg's put on the most wonderful meal for everyone.

It had been such a great day. Everyone enjoyed it. We all got a carrier bag full of goodies from Kellogg's. It was a day to remember.

All that day I had never given my MS another thought and it never played up once, not even when I was wheeling myself round the marathon course for all I was worth. No! For once it let me be a man again. It was a great day, a day I will never forget.

We got home and just did nothing. Tony and I had a look at his car a bit later on and after a bit of messing he got it going and him and Jane went home.

That night I slept the best sleep that I'd had in years. I woke the next morning feeling really good and in great spirits. I phoned Tony to see how he was and Jane answered. I asked to speak to Tony. She laughed and said that he could not walk to the phone he was in that much pain. Through her laughter she told me he'd had to sleep on the sofa all night, as he couldn't manage to climb the stairs. She said that she would try bringing him to our house a bit later that day, as soon as he could move again.

I told Syl about Tony and all that she could do was laugh but that's all that Jane had been doing on the phone as she was telling me - laughing.

Jane brought Tony to our house later that day and as soon as Syl saw him walking up our back path she burst out laughing. He looked at me. I was trying to hold in my laughter and look sympathetic towards him.

Then he said, feeling sorry for himself, 'Look. I'm walking worse than you do.'

He was walking like a man who needed the toilet urgently. You know. That very, very slow legs-together shuffle!

We raised over one hundred and fifty pounds for the baby unit at the hospital that day and Tony was off work for a week.

This was one of the best days of my life, though. I never thought that we would do it but we did, honest. (Ask Tony!)

Chapter Nine

The next couple of months saw Martina leave the department to start a new job at another hospital. Mike, from then on, did my workouts with me with some of the other physiotherapists checking on us from time to time to see that things were going as they should have been, which they were.

There was no way of cutting corners with Mike, he watched everything I did and knew just what to look for. I was once told that if you want to get on then there was no point in cutting corners. That's so right and it would have only been me that I was cheating anyway, so I did what I was told.

It wasn't that I was trying to deliberately cut corners. I was just trying to do more but by trying to increase the amount that I did in the same amount of time, I was cutting out the quality of my exercises. I had done this before and not got very far with it.

I was doing very well, my walking was fairly good with the frame and my back was now much stronger. I wasn't using the wheelchair in the house, just outside to do the shopping with Syl, or for any distances. I wasn't crawling and that was very good news for my knees as they were now on the mend, so all in all, everything was rosy and I was on the up and up for a change.

I was going to physiotherapy only one day a week now to use the equipment and I was doing fine. The department itself was getting very busy, not like when it first opened. Now, besides all the other patients that were going, there was a shortage of staff and space to work in. Once again my exercises were cut short as it was thought that I could do the things I was doing there at home. So I stopped going to the department and started to do the workouts and exercises on the floor at home.

Within a few weeks people started to see the difference in me and in the way that I was walking. I was using my arms more to hold myself up on the Zimmer frame. I didn't have the parallel bars now to practice on, so the quality of my walking was slowly getting worse as I wasn't doing the right sort of exercises that helped me.

I didn't have the equipment now and it was showing in so many ways, so Syl and I went looking for some gyms around the area to see what they could do for us.

We had tried this before and got nowhere but that was a year or so ago so we thought surely there would be something now.

Guess what! Not a single gym in our area would take the chance with me, or there were just too many stairs for me to climb. So it was back to square one again!

For the next few weeks I continued to do my exercises on the floor. My upper-body was fine, my fitness was fine and I wasn't fatiguing. I could go on doing upper-body exercises without any problems but now my legs were beginning to suffer.

Then came the morning that I had been wishing would never come round again. All the work I'd done on my legs was now turning to nothing. My right leg was beginning to play up once again. The toes on that foot would not wiggle, no matter how hard I tried. I was losing my battle. All the hard work that I was doing was amounting to nothing; I needed help, and fast.

Like I say I didn't need help with my upper-body or arms, or even my stamina - just my legs. It was a case of not having smooth floors at home (unlike the gym) to practice my walking. I could easily slide my feet when I walked on the gym floor but on the carpets at home my feet would stick and I would stumble and fall.

Syl and the lads helped me all they could with my exercises but they weren't physiotherapists. They could not see what I needed to be doing, or what I was doing wrong. I needed a new routine, one that would get me going again, one that suited my surroundings, one that would take me that step further.

I really tried hard to adapt things around the house to help me to do the things that I'd been doing at hospital but it just wouldn't work. It was like everything that I so desperately wanted was now slipping away from me once again. I'd been doing so well at hospital, using their equipment, that I was almost there. I just needed a few more weeks exercise, as I was informed by Mike, and I would have been able to cope much better. But that wasn't to be and I was now slipping back, and very quickly.

Syl phoned Maureen the physio-terrorist at work to see if she had any ideas on what we could do. We hadn't seen her for ages and had heard that she was expecting her second baby. She was just about to go on maternity leave on the day that Syl phoned.

Maureen said that I needed to do the exercises that the hospital had given me as well as I was able. I said that it was all well and good doing the exercises but I needed the equipment to do particular exercises properly. What I needed was something new, something that suited the things we had around the house.

She gave us some advice over the phone then popped in later that morning to see how we were getting on. I said that I needed hands-on help to try and put me back on the right track. She agreed. It was wrong of me to say that to Maureen on the day she was leaving but I needed help. Typically, she made a phone call and got one of the local physiotherapists to call in on the Monday.

That following Monday the physiotherapist called in to see me. She did some work with me and we got quite a lot done but I needed to be walking and that was the same old problem: we didn't have the right equipment to do any good. OK, we had the Zimmer frame to use, but it still wasn't any good. I was ready and able to do the things that were needed but, like the physiotherapist said, we didn't have the right equipment.

I was just short of being able to get around the house when I left the hospital but now, through the lack of movement in my legs, I was going downhill. It was as if my legs had forgotten what to do. Now I was making it worse, much worse. Every time that I got on my stairlift to go upstairs I would use my hands to help me.

I would get to the stairlift then use my arms to cushion me to sit down. I wasn't doing it as I had been taught at the hospital: by bending my knees and back, then slowly sitting down. Now I was also starting to physically pick up my right leg in my arms and put it on the footplate of the stairlift as it was a lot quicker to do it that way. Now within a few weeks I had lost all the power in my legs it had taken me so long and hard to achieve.

I had an appointment to see Doctor Sambrook at Withington

Hospital, which I attended. I told him all the things that I had been doing since the last time he saw me. He gave me a good examination and told me that I would benefit from a course of steroids and some intense physiotherapy. This meant that I would have to go into hospital just before Christmas and I wasn't very keen on that idea. We still had a lot of shopping to do for the lads' and family's presents. There was still lots of other little things that needed doing but Syl made it quite clear to me that nothing would go short over the Christmas period; everyone would get their presents and I would be home in time for it all, anyway. So I was put on the waiting list to be admitted to hospital for treatment by Doctor Sambrook.

Within a week there had been a cancellation and I was admitted into hospital. Syl took me up to the ward and waited for me to get settled in. Now, I'm a big softie when it comes to goodbyes so I just looked at Syl, kissed her, then went into the toilet out of the way till she had gone. I was in there about five minutes washing my face trying to hide the tears I'd just cried, like the big girl I am. Then I left to go back to my bed. I looked up the ward to see Syl, still standing at my bedside. I walked up to her - she was smiling away as if there was nothing wrong.

'What you doing still here?' I asked.

She smiled one of her smiles then replied, 'I just thought that I would wait till you came out of the toilet to say goodbye.'

'I've got to go through all that again, now.' I said, shaking my head in disbelief.

We sat on the bed for a few minutes holding hands and laughing, then Syl kissed me and left saying, as she walked down the ward, 'See you tonight love, don't worry.'

Doctor Sambrook came to see me not long after with a few students. He gave me another examination and arranged for me to start having the steroid injections. He also told one of the young doctors with him to see about the physiotherapy.

Throughout that day I saw several different doctors and had several different tests done. They took blood and urine samples, and bent me this way and that. A lot of them were student doctors who asked me if I would mind answering some questions for them about my MS. I didn't mind at all and told them all I could.

There wasn't very much to do on the ward, except to read papers and go for the occasional cigarette in the dayroom. In fact it was totally boring. Syl came that night with the lads. It was so good to see them. I had only been on the ward a few hours and I was already feeling homesick.

Syl asked me how the day had gone and what I had done, who I had seen, and what was going to be done. This was Syl all over, she is fantastic she wanted to know everything. I told her that they had started me on the steroid injections and I was going to have intense physiotherapy. At the time I was having a real problem with my bladder: it wasn't emptying properly again. They were going to send me for an ultra-sound scan and have a few more tests done; I was going to have to have a lot of things done while I was on the ward. Over the next few days, though, I just had tests done and the rest of the time sat about doing not a lot.

I had done no physiotherapy and except for the few students who came to ask me questions about my MS I would have had nothing to do. I asked the physiotherapist on the ward when it was going to be my turn to do some. He kept on telling me that he would be round to me soon, but he never got there. Well if this was a course of intense physiotherapy, then where was it? I had been on the ward now for three days and there weren't any signs of physiotherapy for me.

I was putting on a lot of weight in my face because of the steroids and I was really retaining water around my body, especially in my legs. I asked to see the doctor who came and told me that it was the steroids that was causing the water retention. I asked him if he could do anything about me getting the physiotherapy that I was promised so I could start to get rid of all the weight I was putting on. He said that he would have a word about it for me.

Well he must have because the very next morning a porter came and took me to the gym to have some of that very thing that I had asked them for: physiotherapy!

I did a few loosening up exercises on a bench, a bit of leg-work, a quick stand at the parallel bars then it was time to go back to the ward. I was not best pleased at the amount of work I had done but I was told that was enough as I might fatigue if I was to do anymore.

There was no chance of me fatiguing. I was really up for doing a good workout in the gym, and to show the physiotherapist just what I could do if I was given the chance. My adrenalin had been on overtime; it was racing round my body just at the thought of getting to do something, instead of just sitting around on my bed doing absolutely nothing.

As soon as I went back on the ward I phoned Syl to tell her what had been going on that morning. I was fuming. She told me to calm down and talk to one of the doctors about it. And I did just that. He said that it was all down to being short staffed in the physiotherapy department. I felt a right fool making all that fuss about getting the physiotherapy but it was one of the main reasons I was brought into hospital in the first place. I was told that everything would be fine the week after as there would be more physiotherapists on the wards.

On the Friday I was allowed home for the weekend. Syl came and picked me up with Tony, he had brought her in his car. It was so nice to get home and have something that I liked to eat for a change. Don't get me wrong, the hospital was fine, everything about it was fine, but I was just glad to be home and with my family.

Tony and I went out that night for a pint and while I was out drinking my face went red. It felt as though I was going to explode and I felt so rough with it. The beer and the steroids didn't mix! This was the first time that this had happened to me and I was worried. We went home and I never touched another beer that weekend, I didn't want to take any chances. I had a really good weekend after that except I ended up eating twice as much as I usually did. I told Syl that I didn't want to go back into hospital but she was having none of it. She told me I had to go back if I wanted to get better. Once again she won. Syl and Tony took me back to the ward on the Sunday night and I had my steroid injection while they were there.

The following day the doctors came round to see how everything was going with me. Everything was OK. I sat on the bed talking to one of them about MS and how mine had changed over the past few years. I told him that I hadn't had a remission in all that time. He said that it was more likely that my MS was progressive and not the relapsing, remitting type. I was totally gutted. I just had to know if this was the case, so I asked him when Doctor Sambrook was next on the ward.

Syl came to see me She could see there was something wrong with me: I just wasn't my normal self that night but I didn't tell her what the doctor had said to me about my MS. She kept asking me what the matter was and could she do anything to help me. I just said that I was fed up and wanted to come home, that was all that was the matter, nothing else.

That night I never slept. I just kept thinking about what that doctor and I were talking about and the more I thought of it the more it seemed that I had progressive MS. Well, my bottom lip never stopped all night; I just tucked my head under the sheets and cried and cried.

When I got up in the morning the Sister on the ward said that I was down to have some physiotherapy that day so that cheered me up a bit, to know that I could do something in the exercise line. One good thing that was happening to me was that I was able to walk on the ward. The nice smooth floor made it easy for me to use my frame and get about.

I had my dinner and afterwards a man came to do my physiotherapy with me. We did the work on the bed, a few leg-stretches and some bends then I sat on the edge of the bed and tried to stand up. That was it! End of the intense physiotherapy for another day! Wow I was so exhausted - as if! I asked him why I was only having such a short time to exercise. He said that another physiotherapist hadn't turned in and they were behind in their work for the day. I looked at him, shook my head, and thought what a waste of time.

Doctor Sambrook came on the ward to do his rounds and came over to see me; he asked how I was doing. I told him that I was fine but I needed to be doing more physiotherapy. I just wanted to be doing something positive instead of sitting about doing not a lot. While I was on a roll I then asked him about the possibility that my MS was progressive. He sat on the bed and looked long and hard at me. He could see how upset I was; he was very understanding. We had a good long chat and he thought that, yes, my MS was the progressive type, but he also said that I was managing it very well and doing all the right, positive, things to fight it.

Well, now I knew for sure that the MS I had was the progressive type. Right then and there, at that moment, I needed my Syl, just to hold close to me and make it right, like only she can do at times like this. I was in two minds as to whether to phone her and tell her, or to wait till she came to see me at visiting time and tell her to her face.

I decided to wait until visiting time to tell her. It would be better face to face rather than over the phone. The things that went through my mind while I was waiting for Syl to come and visit were incredible, to say the least. My mind seemed to be jumping years in front wondering just what life had in store for us.

The weather outside was terrible, the snow was thick on the ground and still falling. I was hoping that Syl wouldn't come out in such weather, yet I selfishly wanted her there with me. I kept on looking through the window to see if I could see her but I couldn't. All I could see was the heavy snow falling and the headlights of a few passing cars.

It was visiting time and the people started to come on to the ward. I kept looking toward the door for Syl but I couldn't see her. It seemed that everyone on the ward had a visitor that night except me. I was sitting on my bed looking at one of the crosswords in a paper when I heard, 'Hiya, dad.'

It was Gary and Adam. They came running up to my bed and climbed on and I just threw my arms around them and squeezed them as tightly as I could. Syl and Tony came walking down the ward towards me. I was so glad to see them, it must have shown in my face because Syl put her arms around me and said, 'I bet you thought that we weren't coming.'

She was right, I had thought that. Tony had picked them up and brought them as the weather and roads were so bad. We started talking about this and that; but I was avoiding telling Syl what I had to tell her. I just didn't know how. And then out of the blue she looked at me and said, 'There is something that you are not telling me?'

Tony looked at us both and said that he was just going outside for a cigarette and would be back in a couple of minutes. The lads went with him leaving Syl and me there sitting on the bed able to talk. She looked at me and said, 'Well! What is it then?'

I could feel my throat tightening and my lips going into their "mard-mode". She took hold of my hand, gave it a squeeze then asked, 'What's up, love?'

That did it, I went into my big girl routine. I broke down crying but I was trying to hold it in at the same time. Syl put her arms around me and I sobbed that my MS was progressive. Just like when we first found out that I had MS, we sat there on the bed holding each other tight. Not a word was spoken, not a word needed to be said; we had been here before.

Tony and the lads came back but we never spoke about it. We just carried on as normal telling plenty of jokes and taking the mickey out of just about anything, that's what we did that night.

The next day I discharged myself. The reason being I could do the physiotherapy I was doing there, and more, at home. That is where I wanted to be - at home with my wife and two sons.

I was home a few days and a problem arose. Every time I had a course of steroids I found that my bladder played up and it was very difficult for me to pass water. This was the problem I had now. The amount of water I was retaining was incredible; and I was putting on so much weight again. It got that way that I didn't want to eat the food that was put in front of me at mealtimes in fear of putting on more weight. Syl said that it wasn't the food but the steroids that were causing me to look so overweight. She was right and I knew that but at the time all I could see was this fat thing in the mirror looking back at me, and I was hurting inside because of it.

My feet had swelled to almost twice their normal size; my legs looked like one of those big Russian women shot-putters, huge! My face was so red at times that it looked like a tomato and I had that feeling again, the one where I thought I had two pairs of pants on and couldn't feel anything on my legs. I was feeling so very down inside but doing my best not to let it show.

It was Christmas; a time for good cheer, a time to be happy, a time for families. I carried on as usual being my normal wisecracking smiling self, telling jokes and having a laugh, but it was very hard for me to keep up the pretence. We had done all the shopping and there was nothing left now to do but to eat, drink, and be merry.

We had a fantastic Christmas. The lads, as usual, got all the things they wanted. Syl and I had done our best throughout the year to make sure it was that way for them.

Over the Christmas period I found myself eating and eating, and eating and eating. I just couldn't stop. I always had a good appetite after a course of steroids but this was one appetite that I just couldn't fill. I did no working-out, only a few loosening exercises in a morning and they were just a few, just to show willing. I had lost all interest in doing the thing that had been keeping me going - exercising!

Just after Christmas, Tony and I went for a quiet pint to the local pub. One of the lads in there, who I knew from darts, came over to talk to me and said, 'Good Christmas, Gaz?'

'Yes, very good thanks,' I replied.

'Looks like you ate plenty,' he said laughing.

'Oh cheers, mate,' I said, in a really gob-smacked way.

'Well! Come on, Gaz! You've put on a lot of weight since the last time I saw you.'

That did it! I knew that I was overweight and it was easy to blame the steroids, but I was doing nothing about it. I had been eating like there was no tomorrow and not doing the things that I should have been doing. I could not believe that I had let myself get into this state.

In the space of only a few weeks I had gone from someone who was so keen to be fit, to one who was just happy to plod through. I needed to get my act together and fast, before it was too late to do anything about it. There was a new year a few days away and I was going to be ready for it in mind and in body. There was no way that I was going to carry on the way I had. 1990 was going to be my year.

Chapter Ten

Towards the end of 1989 I had let myself go. I was so full of self-pity that I'd let what I'd been told about my MS being progressive get to me, instead of doing something constructive about it, as I used to when I had a sense of pride in myself. I had just let it get to me without even batting an eyelid to fight back. I had pride in myself before. Then, I would have fought it so what went wrong?

I was now finding myself waiting for something to happen to me. I was getting so scared and frightened inside, just at the thought of it. I was coping when I thought that my MS was the remitting, relapsing type, but now I didn't know what to expect from one day to the next, so I just hid myself inside myself.

Until the night I had a rude awakening in the pub. God! I had become so weak. It wasn't me to let that happen, I was stronger than that.

So 1990 started with me back to my determined self; I was so full of purpose again. January saw me go back on a diet and start to do some very serious exercising. I was using weights and doing lots of upper-body work, leg-work, and really working hard on my stamina exercises. I would use the stairlift to go up the stairs, then I would walk down them. I would do this ten to twenty times a day, just to try strengthening up my legs. I would sit on the floor in the kitchen, then try to get up without using my hands.

Social Services had a ramp built at the back to make it easier for me to walk in from my car. There were also two bars, one either side of the door so I used these like a set of parallel bars. It was so good to practice my walking again without using the Zimmer frame, but the weather was bad most of the time so I could only do it every now and then.

I was still having trouble with my bladder, which caused a lot of problems. I would no sooner get on the floor to do some exercises than I would have to get up again and go to the toilet. This meant that I had to get to the stairlift, go upstairs, do what I had to do, then get back on the stairlift, go downstairs and carry on from where I left off.

This used to drive me crazy. In fact there were times that I just took the pain. I would be wearing the clamp and get the urge to go to the toilet just as I was doing some leg-work on the floor. I would clamp it shut and just carry on till I had finished my exercising.

I know! I know! This was a crazy thing to do but it was better than having to keep running up the stairs. I tried to cut down on the things I was drinking but that made little difference. I wasn't emptying my bladder fully and I was getting what seemed like infection after infection, which caused me no end of pain and discomfort, and I do mean pain and lots and lots of discomfort.

Syl bought me several different things to try and help with the emptying of my bladder; things that I had tried in the past, like water tablets and cranberry juice. They helped me in the sense that they made me go to the toilet but they didn't help me to totally empty my bladder. I still had the feeling that I needed to go.

I had to work round it, like when I first became incontinent; there were days when it suited me fine not needing to go to the toilet for ages, then there were the days that I had no sooner got off than I was back on it.

It was just a matter of getting it right on the day, and I was getting to be a dab hand at it. I was getting back on top of my life and doing quite well in the things that I was doing. My fitness was on the up and up and I was losing the weight that I had put on, but I still needed that push to help me to where I was six months or so ago. So, I went to the doctor's to see what he could do for me. He wrote off to have me put on the list for some home physiotherapy.

It was the middle of February, and the weather was not too clever to say the least. I was getting out and about thanks to the wheelchair and I was doing quite nicely, all in all. There was something on at the local theatre that the lads wanted to see so as a surprise Syl and I went to book at the ticket office in Ashton.

I was at the counter in my wheelchair ordering the tickets and Syl was standing next to me. I passed the money through the window to the lady who was serving us and she passed me the tickets. It was quite a stretch to do this but I did it, then the lady said something to me and passed me my change. I dropped a five-pound note on the floor just in front of the window, so I leant forward in my chair to pick it up.

Well, the wheelchair did a forward wheelie and I got my head stuck in the front of the counter. Laugh! I thought that Syl wouldn't stop. She was rolling about in fits of laughter, and there I was twisting and turning, ever so carefully, trying to get my head from under the counter.

Well! I must have looked a right wazzock! When I finally got up the lady who had been serving me was gone. There was just an empty chair where she'd been and a giggle coming from behind a screen. I was the talking point and the butt of all Syl's joke for weeks; she really went to town on me after that. Yes, life was getting back to normal, well and truly. Things for once were going right for us; we had a smile back on our faces.

After a few weeks I was having physiotherapy at home again. This time it wasn't Maureen the physio-terrorist, she was still on maternity leave, having had a little boy, called Philip.

I was given a referral to have treatment back at the Ashton Hospital Physiotherapy Department.

I was so pleased to be going back to have my physiotherapy at the hospital with all their equipment. This was really turning out to be my year in a big way. I had to see a physiotherapist there called Claire. She was new to me and had only been there for a short time. The department had quite a few new staff: from receptionists to the physiotherapists themselves.

Quite a lot had changed over the months that I had not been going for treatment. I was sat in the waiting area till my name was called out; I saw a few old faces I knew from the last time I was there. I was speaking to one member of staff when my name was called.

I went over to the lady who had called my name. Syl and the member of staff walked over with me. 'This is Gary,' the member of staff said.

'And I'm Claire,' the other physiotherapist replied.

I started to wheel myself towards the gym.

'No, this way.' Claire said. 'We are in the wax room.'

We went into the wax room and I was asked to get on one of the electronic beds that were there. On that first day I had to be assessed to see what I could and couldn't do and what sort of work needed to be done with me.

I did the usual things like sitting on the side of the bed and stretching out as far as I could, then I did lots of work on my legs. I was lying on my back with my knees bent and taking one leg at a time out to the side and back.

Then it was bridging. Staying on my back with my knees still bent. I would then lift my bottom off the bed. I found this very hard to do with all the leg-work and stretching I had just done. Before I had gone back to the department I thought that I was fit and doing well, how wrong I was.

Claire asked me to show her how I walked using the Zimmer frame. I only took a few steps and she told me to sit back down. She told me that she would start me on some stretching exercises for my back; all the loosening exercises I was already doing I was to carry on with as normal.

The strengthening exercises I was going to do consisted of lots of bridging and stretching, plus I was to sit on the side of the bed and let my shoulders and back slump, then sit up straight again without using my hands or jerking.

This was very, very hard to do. As soon as I went to straighten up I would either jerk up or use my hands, so I was told to hold my arms out in front of me. No way could I do this. I was just so weak in my back muscles and lower-body. All the things that I had concentrated on the last time I was at this physiotherapy department had gone; now it was back to that old square one again.

Claire gave me another appointment for later that same week. When I got home I was totally disgusted with myself at not being able to do the things I was asked to do. Well, that did it! My determination to do better the next time that I went really spurred me on. I was pushing my body to the limit. I was getting up at seven each morning and starting to exercise right away. I wasn't going out to the shops or anywhere, I was just staying in and doing the things that I was told to do, and more.

Things don't improve by themselves. I was fighting for

everything that I had and the fight was back on, right there and then. I couldn't let myself slip as I had done only a couple of months earlier, so I pushed and pushed myself every minute of the day.

I wasn't fatiguing, that was one thing that I had no problems with. Once a day I would do a really big workout to music. I would put my favourite tape in the stereo, get on the floor, press play and start to do my exercises. I would get carried away listening to the music. It made the work seem a lot easier. In fact the time passed a lot quicker doing it this way, so much so that I found I ended up doing more.

I would go upstairs into our bedroom, sit on the side of the bed, and start to do my stretching exercises, then the back-strengthening and bridging work. These were the hardest exercises that I had to do and doing them on the bed made them even more difficult.

Then came the day that I had to go to hospital for my physiotherapy. I was, as usual, looking forward to doing my working-out. Claire took me straight into the wax room and we started to do my loosening up exercises first.

When I started to do my back-work and bridging she told me she could see an improvement from the other day. This made me feel great! The hard work I had been doing at home was paying dividends. I had put a lot of effort into and it was showing.

She asked me to do some different things then. I was asked to sit on the side of the bed and raise my right foot off the ground. This was hard to do; straight away I grasped the side of the bed with my hands, to give me some leverage. Claire was like lightning. She got a hold of my hands and told me to put them on top of my head and told me to keep them there.

I tried again. This time my body leant to the left so I could use my hips to help me get my foot off the floor. Even doing this I could hardly manage to raise my foot a couple of inches. Then it was the turn of my left foot. This one wasn't really that bad, I raised it a couple of inches off the floor without too much trouble. Once again I hadn't realised that I could not do these simple things.

When I walked on my frame I would swing my legs out from the hips. I wasn't raising them off the floor, as I should have, or I was sliding them along. I wasn't "walking through", as she explained. I thought that I had gone through all this once and got the better of it, but I had slipped back. The sad thing was I hadn't even noticed.

I had picked up so many bad habits over the months that my body was just not right. Different parts of me were now compensating for the parts that no longer worked, or were just too weak to do so. In things like lifting my legs off the floor I was using my hands or my hips, anything but my leg muscles.

As I have said before, I used to pick my legs up with my hands and put them on the stairlift because it was quicker to do it that way. This had now grown into a habit. I was doing it as part of my everyday routine of getting about the house.

I had to get out of this set of bad habits I had got myself into and find the right way of doing things again. Claire told me that my quadriceps and hamstrings were very weak and needed working on, but for now I was to concentrate on my back and get that stronger again. This was in addition to all the other work I had been doing with her.

I asked Claire if I could use the parallel bars to practice my walking. She said that was out for now as she thought it best just to do the things that she had set me.

Over the next few weeks I worked as hard as I had ever worked in my life. Every day I did my exercises without fail. I would walk down the stairs after using my stairlift; I would use the bars on the ramp out at the back to also practice my walking. I was doing very, very well. In fact I would go as far as to say I was good, and I knew it! I was so confident in doing my exercises that I was getting cocky. Too cocky!

Once I was walking down the stairs with both my hands on the handrails, I started to push myself up on the rails so that my feet never touched the stairs. I thought that I was clever. Then slip! And Oops! Bang! Crash! Bang! I hit the bottom of the stairs and lay there in a heap.

Syl rushed from the kitchen to where I was lying and said, 'What happened?'

I looked up at her and said, 'I fell.'

'Did you miss a step?' she enquired, all sympathetic-like. 'No, love. I hit every one!'

'Oh, funny. I won't bother asking in future,' she said, as she walked away leaving me lying there trying to get up.

I didn't hurt myself physically, only my pride was hurt, but

115

I never tried it again.

The next time I went to the physiotherapy department Claire had a surprise for me. I was going to do my work in the gym and have a go on the parallel bars. This was great; the very thing I wanted. I got out of my wheelchair at one end and walked to the other to show Claire how well I was doing. I thought that I did fine. Wrong!

Claire said that we would now do it the proper way. I had to walk back to my wheelchair and now lift my feet off the ground, one foot in front of the other, instead of sliding them as I had just done. This was very hard to do and my legs really felt it, too. This was going to be hard.

Over the next few weeks, every time I used the parallel bars, Claire would move my feet in front of me to help me to stop swinging my legs from my hips, or sliding them along the floor. This took time and it was so very hard to do as I was now so set in the way that I had been walking, it was going to be an all new experience for me to learn the correct way of walking again. I had been walking incorrectly for such a long time now and I was so used to doing it that way.

When I walked on the parallel bars my hands gripped tight and my arms still took most of the weight, as my legs were still not that strong, but I was moving in the right direction and improving at a good steady pace - and that was all that mattered.

Claire was pleased with my progress and so was I. This time I wasn't trying to rush things; I was taking it nice and steady and doing quality work and not taking the quick route as I normally did.

Claire made me feel that the work I was doing was beneficial and she really inspired me to go for it, as did Mike when he was helping me with Claire; they were a good team. Claire was very nice to Syl and me, we had a good few laughs and jokes but that didn't stop her from doing her job, and she was very good at that.

I asked her if I could one day go in the pool as I had been in before and done well. She said that if I kept on improving the way that I had been then she would see what she could do. That was like music to my ears, the thought of going back into the hydrotherapy pool and walking without a frame, oh yes!

I did my walking at the department and I was doing some on the ramp at home. Syl would help me to move my feet just as Claire did at the hospital. She was getting such a dab hand at the old physiotherapy that I was thinking of getting her a job there. Just kidding,

Syl!!

She had seen so much work being done with me over the years that she had picked quite a lot of it up; she was good at doing my leg-work with me and would help me whenever I needed her to. And there were plenty of times that I needed her help, especially at this time.

I found that through doing the exercises my back was a lot stronger now and I was standing without stooping forwards. The walking I was doing using my frame was good, very good. So much so that one day I said to Syl, 'I'm going to try to walk outside.'

'I think that's pushing it, Gaz,' Syl said, reluctantly.

'No, trust me, I can do it! Honestly, I really can,' I said.

'OK, where to?' she asked.

'From the back of the house to the front,' I said, confidently.

With that we went into the back garden. Syl got my wheel-chair out of the car.

'What's that for?' I asked.

'Just in case,' she said.

With that I started to walk down the drive and carried on and on. I didn't stop till I reached the front of the house.

I was over the moon at what I had just done, so much so that my eyes went misty. Syl told me to sit down in my wheelchair to rest so I did. I was absolutely exhausted.

It had taken me ages to do that walk and it took all the energy I had to do it. I almost asked Syl for the wheelchair several times but I just kept on going. This was something I had to finish and I did; I didn't ask for the wheelchair - that would have been giving in and to give in wasn't on the day's menu.

Syl was so proud she kept on saying, 'You did it! You did it!'

One of our neighbours walked past and made a comment about me being out of my wheelchair. Syl straight away said, 'You just missed him walking.'

We went round to the back, I even walked up the ramp and into the house, I was feeling that good that day. The feeling that I had was fantastic, it lasted for days and days. I think I told everyone I knew what I had done, I was that chuffed with myself.

I could not wait to go to the hospital for my next appointment to tell them all in the physiotherapy department what I had done, and I did. As soon as I walked through the doors I started telling everyone, even the patients that were in there for treatment got the story told to them.

Claire said that I had done very well but not to overdo it just take it easy. To me I was getting my life back and I was enjoying every minute of it. I didn't see it as overdoing things but I suppose she was right; I was wanting to run before I could even walk, as usual! We did plenty of work in the gym that day and for once I was glad to get finished. My legs were starting to ache. This may sound crazy to you but it was the most wonderful feeling to have this ache. It was a feeling that I had not had in a very long time, a feeling of not exactly pain but the feeling you get when you have had a long day at work, and all you want to do is put your feet up. That was the feeling. I even put my feet in a bowl of hot water to soak them when we got in and wiggled my toes, too. Then I put them up on the stool for a rest that they well deserved.

That night I had a really good sleep. It was so wonderful, everything was going to plan, my life once again was beginning to mean something. I was back to my very best.

The next time I went to see Claire at the hospital we did lots of walking in the gym with a Zimmer frame, then I was on the parallel bars, then on the benches; I really had a good workout that day. Claire could not believe the amount of work that I had got through on the one day. She said that she was so pleased that she would give me a try in the hydrotherapy pool to see how I went on. She said that there was an appointment for early the following morning if I wanted it. I was ready, willing, and, yes, able. I'd be there first thing in the morning.

We were at the hospital for just gone nine o'clock the next morning. I was really excited about going back into the pool. Claire met Syl and me in the waiting area and showed us to the changing rooms. I was ready in no time as I already had my shorts on under my clothes. Claire pushed me in my wheelchair to the poolside. I wanted to walk down the steps into the water but that would have been too dangerous, she said, so I had to use the hoist just as I had done the last time I was in there. I only had to wear one float this time, though, so I didn't look like someone from a shipwreck!

I was put on the hoist and lowered into the water where Claire was waiting for me. Syl was at the side of the pool watching and cracking jokes at my expense.

As soon as I got off the hoist I did a bit of a swim, then stood up at the side holding on till I was told what to do. Claire told me to hold on to the side of the pool and lift my right leg as high as I could and hold it there.

I did quite well. I was really surprised to be honest, then I did the left leg. This was very good, I was having no problems with this one at all. I was told to walk without holding on to the side of the pool, and I did, managing a few feet. This really was a great feeling to walk again without any help.

I had done this sort of thing before in the pool and I felt the same sort of emotions as I had then. I asked Claire if this was just going to be a one-off thing or was I going to be able to use the pool to do exercises more often. She said that she could not see any problem in me using the pool from time to time because it helped strengthen my legs, and that would help me with my walking.

I was so pleased to hear this. I didn't want to be told that it was no good for me as I had MS and might "fatigue" and couldn't go in again. So over the next few weeks I used the pool quite a few times and it really did me the world of good, in my walking, and in me personally. I felt I was free from the frame again for those few precious minutes I was in there.

Late one afternoon I got a phone call from Claire. She said that there was going to be a demonstration of a new piece of equipment and would I like to take part. I said that I would love to and asked when was it going to be. She said that it was that night after the department closed, so I only had an hour or so to get ready and get there.

We had tea and went down to the hospital to the demonstration. When we got there all the physiotherapists were still there and a lot of people we didn't know. Some people were already having treatment from the new piece of equipment. Claire told me that it was a new, electronic muscle-stimulator that was being used on them. I had to wear my shorts as they were going to be using the stimulator on my legs, which meant that I could not use a leg-bag. I had to use the dreaded clamp instead.

I was asked to get ready and get on one of the beds that were there. There was a very "official" feel to the demonstration; not like my normal physiotherapy.

There was an audience which included all the physiotherapists from the hospital. I wheeled myself to the side of the bed and got onto it. The lady who was doing the demonstration was one of the top physiotherapists in the country, I was told.

She asked the physiotherapists for volunteers to do the exercise. Three physiotherapists I knew stood up: Claire, then one of the male physiotherapists from the department, and Sue, who was in charge.

They wired me to the machine, which was about the size of a Walkman radio, and switched it on at a low level. Then it was slowly increased. I could feel my muscles starting to pulsate; the machine was working my quadriceps. I could see them moving but all I could feel was a slight tingling sensation.

Then I had to lie on my stomach so they could put the wires from the machine on my hamstrings. This was very uncomfortable to do because of the clamp sticking into me. I was asked if I was comfortable by the lady in charge. Well, I didn't want to say that I was wearing the clamp, so I said that I was.

The machine was turned on. They started on a low level, as before, until it started to move my hamstrings. The lady said that she would leave this one about fifteen minutes.

Oops! Well, I was OK for about five of those minutes, then I got the urge to use the toilet. I had to get to the clamp and clamp it down somehow while I was on my stomach but also try not to draw attention to myself. Not a very easy thing to do, especially when there are lots of people looking and smiling at you.

It was like Mission Impossible. You know, "The tape will self-destruct in five seconds.". Only this time the tape was my bladder, and three seconds had passed!

I slid my hand under my body, all the time smiling trying not to be noticed. Somehow, I just managed to do it in time. I felt more at ease once I had done this. I then started to relax.

I was asked if I could lift the heel of my foot to touch my bottom. I tried whilst the machine was still working and almost did it with my left. I even moved my right leg off the bed, which was a very big thing for me to have done. This machine was marvellous. It was doing things to my muscles that I couldn't do any more. This really was a magic box!

The following day when I went for my physiotherapy everyone was talking about the night before and the demonstration of the machine. I was told the machine had done so much for so many different illnesses, for so many people, in so many different ways.

For me? Well, it had helped me to almost touch my bottom with the heel of my foot, and it had worked my quadriceps. The department was going to get two of these machines in the not-so-distant future and I asked Claire how much they were to buy.

I couldn't believe it when she said that they were over three hundred pounds each. They were only like little radios, and they worked off the same sort of batteries, too. How do they come up with these sort of prices for things like this? It's totally crazy! I just couldn't believe it.

It was the beginning of June. The weather was on the up and up and just the sort of weather to do a marathon. I told Claire that I would like to help raise funds to buy another of the machines for the department. If I did a marathon again that would be the perfect way to raise the sort of money that we needed to have.

All I needed now was someone to do the marathon with me, someone who had done it before, but who?

Chapter Eleven

Tony! Yes my lovable brother-in-law, Tony. He was the perfect choice, but he would take some persuading, especially after last year and the pain he went through.

Well! He was my mate, my buddy, my pal, and this was for another good cause, but I would still have to con him into it. So that night when he came round to our house to go for a quiet pint I would put it to him. Well, in a roundabout sort of way.

I already had the forms for the marathon, and also the sponsorship ones, so I took them out with me to the pub to sort of "leave" them where Tony could see them.

The pub was full. All the lads we knew were in there playing pool, darts or cards. We were having a great night. Tony went to the toilet so I thought that it was a good time to get the sponsorship forms out and asked some of the lads to sponsor me in the marathon.

I told them that it was in aid of the machine for the hospital's Physiotherapy Department. They were all for it. I had no problem in getting sponsors. The lads were putting their names down on the forms without me really asking. They were filling in the spaces on the forms really quickly. Tony walked back into the vault; he was patted on the back by some of the lads. He laughed and shook a few people's hands as he came and sat back down.

'What's all that about?' he asked me, looking baffled.

'Oh, didn't I tell you? You're, erm, er, down to do a marathon with me,' I said, keeping my head down

He went quiet for a minute, then, 'Oh no! Oh no, no way!' he said, shaking his head.

'Tony, it's for a good cause. The hospital.'

'No way, I said! I was off work for over a week last time we did one. Remember?' He started to tremble with shock.

'But, Tony! You won't be doing it on your own this time, mate.'

His little brain started to tick: 'What do you mean?'

'Just that I will get you some help.'

'Oh yes! Who?'

'I don't know yet, but trust me.'

He seemed to calm down a bit then and he even stopped shaking.

'OK! I will do it but only, and I mean only, if you get someone else to do it as well.'

'No problems. Trust me.'

Now all I needed was to find someone else, but who?

The very next day I got a phone call from my nephew, Timothy, who lives in Wales to say that he was coming down to Manchester the following weekend. Now, our Tim is a body-builder and weightlifter, and a very fit lad. He would do anything for his uncle Gaz, even run in a marathon. So I asked him. Straight away he said, "Yes". He was delighted that I had asked him to run the marathon with Tony and me. Now if I could get one more person to do it with us that would mean more money to get the machine; plus, each person would only have to do one lap each with me. But I was struggling to get that third person.

Over the following week I did my exercises at the hospital and I got plenty of people to sponsor me. I asked one or two people if they would like to run the last lap with me but I had no luck.

Tim called at our house that weekend and we got talking about old times and things that had been happening. Then we got on to the subject of the marathon and who we could get to do the last lap with me. Our Tim came up with the perfect person: Roy, his dad. Roy had run the London Marathon and plenty of others to boot; he was ideal for the job. I had forgotten all about Roy. Tim said that he would do it; there was no problem now. Everything was set, all we had to do was the marathon itself.

The day of the marathon came around quickly. It seemed like only yesterday that Tony and I had done the last one. It was very busy, there were lots of people there to do the marathon and to just watch and enjoy the day. It seemed that all my family was there to watch us, too. There was my mum, my sister Maureen, Syl and the lads, Jane - Tony's wife, and all Roy's family.

There were lots of us and everyone was really enjoying the day. We were in the canteen having a drink and chat and I thought, let's have a joke with Tony. So I said, 'Tony, I need the toilet. Give me a hand to get there, mate.'

'No way! Ask your Tim!' he replied, turning away from me.

'Come on, Tony. Just give us a hand to get into that toilet over there.'

It was the same toilets that we had a problem in at the last marathon.

'Forget it. You and ****** toilets!' he said.

Everyone started laughing. They all knew about the last time we were there. We carried on having a laugh for a few minutes more, then we got the call to line up for the marathon.

Tony was going to do the first lap, then our Tim, then Roy. We were all looking forward to doing it and just like the last marathon, Tony got us near the front and got off well.

We did the first lap at a nice easy pace. We kept stopping for a chat and a cigarette and generally messing about and after quite some time we reached the end of the first lap so our Tim could start the second lap. At times I thought he was going to just run with me sat in the chair under his arm. He was a really strong lad; he even stopped on the way round to help someone to put the rubber tyre back on their wheelchair.

Our Tim really enjoyed doing it. He said, 'Last one now, mate,' as he handed over to Roy.

Wow! Roy was like Billy Whiz; I found it hard to push my wheels he was going that fast. Roy kept on telling me to keep my hands off the wheels and inside the wheelchair, which I found very hard to do. I wanted to help as much as I could, but with Roy, and the rate he was going I was only slowing him down, but I didn't care so I carried on. It wasn't a race, was it?

Well we got the marathon done in a very good time, even after the first lap when Tony and I kept on stopping for a cigarette. We got our medals and raised over three hundred and fifty pounds for that day's work, which meant that we had enough money to buy the machine for the department.

I gave the cheque to Claire on behalf of us all and she was over the moon, to say the least, at what we had done. It was such a good feeling to have done something like this and for such a good cause. The machine would help so many people in so many different ways.

In August we took the lads out to Knowsley Safari Park with Tony and Jane. I let Tony drive my car around the park, as I was watching out for the animals with Gary and Adam. There was so much to see. We got to this particular part of the park which had buffaloes and other similar animals.

Tony turned to me and asked, 'Are they deer?'

I looked and replied, 'I don't know, there's no price on them.'

That set the tone for the rest of the day. It was a great day out. I was in my wheelchair going round the fun-fair but I managed to walk into the toilets and the cafeteria.

This had been really great for me to do. My life was really turning the corner: I was getting the freedom that I had so long waited for. I seemed to have got back on top of myself again. The MS was behaving, too. It had not played up for ages.

We got home that night and Tony and Jane decided to stay the night, as we were all so very tired after such a long day. Jane was now well overdue with the baby but showing no signs of having it. Tony was getting very anxious about it all and it was beginning to show that night.

The following morning after breakfast everyone but me went down to the wood for a walk. When they got back after an hour or so everyone was laughing at Jane because she had tripped over a twig and fallen. She was the talking point all through Sunday dinner. Then, Ouch! She got pains. She told Tony to ring the hospital for her but he couldn't, he was so excited. He asked me to ring and pretend that I was him so I did.

I phoned the hospital and told them what had been going on. The lady on the other end of the phone wanted to take some details. 'What is her name?' she asked.

'Jane,' I said.

'Jane what?'

'Jane, what's your surname?' I shouted.

'McGovern,' she shouted back to me from the other side of the room.

'It's McGovern,' I told the lady.

'Address?' she then asked.

'What's your address, Jane?' Jane shouted her address to me.

Well! I could hear the lady on the other end of the phone tutting and mumbling as if to say this guy's totally dumb! I didn't care.

After that it took ages for me to give all Jane's details to the lady. Jane and I were shouting to each other across the living room, but in the end I got it all done.

Tony had to take Jane to Wythenshawe Hospital where, two days later, she gave birth to a baby girl. Syl and I went to see mother and baby the next day. Both were fine. They named her Caroline.

After a few days in hospital they were both allowed home so I went to pick them up as Tony's car was off the road again, needing to be repaired.

To get in their house you had to climb a very steep flight of stairs, which I did. It took me a while but I managed it without any real problems. To be able to do things like this again was wonderful. It was all due to the work that I had done at the Physiotherapy Department.

I was really getting around a lot better and my walking had improved no end. I was doing the walk from the back of our house to the front regularly now.

Everything was going great. I celebrated my birthday on the seventeenth and then Tony's on the eighteenth. Then towards the end of August I got the start of another water infection. It came on gradually through the day. I was OK for most of the day, then towards the night-time it started.

I would start to shiver then get flu-like symptoms. Then the terrible pains would start in my lower-back. I went to bed and Syl made me a hot toddy but that did no good, so she had to send for the doctor. I was prescribed a course of antibiotics and told to drink plenty of fluids. I was shivering terribly yet I was sweating. My body was very hot. Syl was told to keep the blankets off me to keep my temperature down, which she did, as she nursed me all through the night.

Within a couple of days I was on the mend and getting about the house again. I had to finish the hospital physiotherapy as I had made good progress. It was all down to the exercises and hard work that I did in the pool and gym, working with Claire and Mike. The hard work that they had done with me, that's what got me on my feet again.

I was told that I would be put on the list for follow-up treatment by the Community Physiotherapists at home. However, before I was finally discharged as one of Claire's patients, she made an appointment for me to see a Doctor Walton at the hospital.

Doctor Walton was the rehabilitation doctor and was based at the Floyd Unit, Birch Hill Hospital, in Rochdale, but she held clinics once a month at Tameside.

She was very nice. She gave me a good examination and asked me lots of questions about my MS. I would see a great deal of her over the next seven years, about MS and other things.

Over the next couple of weeks I really concentrated on getting myself fit again after yet another water infection. This one had taken a lot out of me and I was feeling low and a bit on the miserable side to say the least. So much so that Syl told me I had two heads: one for in the house and one for outside. I knew what she meant. I was so down when I was in the house I never really seemed to be smiling, but as soon as I went out, whether it was to the shops with Syl, or to visit friends and family, I was smiling. Then, I always had a smile on my face and would laugh and joke about almost anything.

I was keeping myself busy in the house doing lots of exercises through the day but I was so bored I needed to occupy my mind with something. I was still using the handrails on the ramp as a set of parallel bars and I was still walking down the stairs in the house, slowly, using the banisters and wall as support. I was doing anything and everything to keep busy and in shape but I was so bored and getting nowhere fast.

I wasn't making the progress that I had been at the hospital when I was using their equipment and pool. I was hoping that by this time I would have been back using just a walking-stick but was this a pipe dream I had, something that I couldn't reach?

Maureen, the physio-terrorist, called one morning to do some work with me. This was the first time that Syl and I had seen her since she had come back to work. We did lots of upper-body, floor and leg exercises. Then I did some walking on my Zimmer frame, which she said was OK. She made an appointment to come the following week to do some more work with me. I told her that I was bored with the things I was doing and that I needed more to do, something that would take me that step closer to my dream.

At the time I was back to doing one thousand sit-ups a day, plus two to three hundred push-ups. Then there was all the other exercises I did with the weights and on the floor, stretching. In fact I was in the best shape that I had ever been in and I didn't really need to do more. I was just pushing myself to the limit and beyond, trying to get back something that was just out of my reach. I was trying too hard. To be honest I was scared, very scared. I just wanted to stay the way I was, fit and mobile, and not lose the things that I had fought so hard to get back. Things like my toes wiggling again when I wanted them to, and being able to lift my feet off the floor instead of shuffling them along. I had these things back and I was so scared that I might lose them again, and not be able to get them back.

I was able to play football with my sons again. OK, it was on their computer, but I was playing with them. I was dressing myself now and getting in and out of the bath without any problems and I was so thankful to wake every morning and still be able to do these things. I was dreading that day when the toes stopped wiggling and the feet didn't lift. This was why I needed to do more and more - I was trying to stay strong and fit, to stop that day from catching up with me once again.

It was December and the lads were in different plays at school. In addition to that, Adam had been practising his gymnastics. He went once a week after school to practice this routine and he was so looking forward to doing it, and to Syl and me going to watch it at the coffee morning. He had been talking about it for weeks. He told us just how good it was and how hard he had worked on this very special routine. He was eight and seemed to be in everything that was going on at school. He just loved to be part of it all. I would ask him, when he got in from his practice, what he had done but all he would say was that it was a secret!

Well it finally came to the day of the coffee morning and all the mums and dads were there, sitting in the children's little chairs. I was the only one in a big chair, mind you it had wheels on it, and it was my own. The head teacher welcomed all the parents to the special morning then introduced the gymnastics class. They all marched in: stiff-backed, heads held high, arms swinging at their sides, each looking out for their parents. They formed a circle in the middle of the hall where the mats had been laid out for them, then they went into their routine.

Their little faces as they did their rolls and jumps was so lovely to see, each one trying to catch their parents' eyes.

Adam did his roll then stood up looking over to where Syl and I were sitting. He had his tongue in his cheek and a smile as wide as the Severn Bridge, he was so chuffed at what he had done.

Well! That was it. I went into my "mard-mode" then. My lips went all limp and the tears started clogging up my eyeballs, I was so proud. I couldn't see anything after that. I had totally gone to pot.

Syl said, 'Aw! Look, Gaz!'

That did it the sniffles started, so I made a quick grab for the hanky out of my pocket and pretended to blow my nose. Syl was the same, as were a lot of other mums and dads that morning. Those weeks of training had amounted to: two jumps, some balancing on one leg, a skip and a head-roll; but what a performance they all gave. Brilliant.

Gary brought home his work from the year at school. On one piece of work he had designed a wheelchair. No! Not an ordinary wheelchair, but one especially for me. It had everything I needed on it: an umbrella for when it rained; an ashtray for when I wanted a cigarette; electric lights for in the dark. I didn't need to wheel myself, either. It was an electric racer with a fishing-rod holder and a bag to put things in.

Everything that I needed or wanted was on this chair. He could have drawn anything that day but it had to be that special chair for me; this made me feel so very, very proud of him.

We went to see the lads in their plays. They were wonderful. Gary was the back end of a cow and he played the part fantastically, swishing his tail like a true professional. Adam was a Christmas tree; he walked up to his place on the set then, as he was walking back off, got stuck in the doors, but like a true actor he brought the house down. Well nearly.

It was a wonderful Christmas. It had been a wonderful year. We had had a great time. I was in good health and on my feet, Syl and the lads were happy and all was well. Yes, 1990 had been a good year and we were going into the new one in good shape for once.

Chapter Twelve

1991 started well. I was doing fine in myself but my walking was starting to suffer. I couldn't use the ramp outside to practice my walking, as the weather was too bad and very icy. I wasn't walking down the stairs as much, either, as my legs were not as strong as they had been. Now my arms were having to take all the strain instead.

I had an appointment to see Doctor Walton at Tameside hospital at the end of January for a check-up. She thought that I would benefit from some intense physiotherapy, as I responded well to that. She referred me to the Physiotherapy Department.

Within a couple of weeks I was back on the parallel bars doing my walking. Claire had left to go to another hospital and there were a lot of new staff in the department. I was now being treated by a physiotherapist called Sue, who watched every little thing I did and was just as eagle-eyed as Claire and Mike had been with me in the past.

I was doing very well with my walking again after only a few weeks on the parallel bars. They were a lot better for my walking practice than the Zimmer frame I was using at home. I was a lot stronger in my legs. All they needed was the use of the equipment and because of it I was a lot better on my frame in the house, and down the ramp. The only thing was that the ramp had started to fall apart because of the bad weather.

One night as I was coming in from the car, walking on my frame, I fell. Part of the ramp had broken and there was a hole. The front wheel of my Zimmer frame went into it and I ended up falling, with my right leg stuck under me. I was lying on my ankle and in terrible pain. We got into the house, after Syl had brought my wheel-chair from the car for me to use the rest of the way. My foot swelled up to twice its normal size and it was going black and blue. I was in real agony.

Syl told me to go to the hospital to have it X-rayed. But it was getting late and I didn't want to have to drag the lads out at that time of night, so I said that I would go in the morning when we had dropped the lads off at school. I had a really rough night with it. I just couldn't get to sleep, the pain was so bad. Syl propped it up with pillows, when I got in bed, to ease the pain but that did no good. I just sat on the side of the bed for most of the night trying to find some ease from the pain.

As soon as we dropped the lads off at school the next morning we went to the Accident and Emergency Department at Tameside hospital. I had to see the Triage Nurse first. She said that there would be a long time for us to wait to see a doctor. It was just gone nine-thirty and was very busy. I had been up most of the night with the pain and taken loads of painkillers so I was feeling exhausted.

Syl had strapped my foot up in a cold-water bandage to try to take the swelling away. I had no boot on my right foot and the leg of my jeans was rolled up to my knee. My name was called out and I was shown into a cubicle to wait for the doctor. He walked in shortly after. He looked as though he'd just had a rough night himself. I wasn't in a very good mood, to say the least, because of all the pain and waiting.

He was reading my chart, then he looked at me and said, 'What's the problem?'

'I fell and hurt my ankle on the ramp at home,' I said.

'Which ankle is it?'

He was looking straight at me. I could not believe what he had just said. I was in my wheelchair with the leg of my jeans rolled up to my knee, with no boot or sock on, just this swollen black and blue foot on show.

So I said, God only knows why, 'Take a wild guess!'

Well he had a face like a smacked ass. He was not a happy

bunny. He took hold of my ankle with both hands, had a look, and asked me where it hurt. Well! After I climbed down from the ceiling I told him in no uncertain terms where it hurt.

Now I get on with anybody, but this guy, well, his bedside manner was something to be desired, even by me. I know the man was tired but he could have been more sympathetic and bloody gentle.

He sent me for an X-ray, which I later took back to him. This time he was a bit more cheerful till me and my big mouth said to him, 'We got off on the wrong foot there, doctor.'

Oh dear! Hush my mouth. He was not happy with that one, his face told me that. He didn't have to say a word it was so very, very, obvious.

He looked at my X-rays and said, 'Your foot is broken in three places.'

So, once again, I tried to lighten him up: 'Well, I won't be going to those places again!'

Not a titter, not a smile, just a, 'Hmmm, yes, right. You need it plastering.'

I bet he wished he could have plastered my gob up, too. I waited in the cubicle till a nurse came in and took Syl and me to the plaster room. The lady who was doing the plastering was a very nice person and jolly. She said that because I was not too good on my feet she wouldn't use plaster of Paris. Instead she'd use fibreglass, as it was much lighter.

I asked her, while she was doing it, if there was any chance of her mending a broken fishing rod I had. She thought that was funny; at least she had a sense of humour.

When she had done my leg she said, 'How does that feel?'

'Great,' I said.

'Not too tight, then?'

'No, no problem. Except it's on the wrong leg.'

'Oh no! You're joking!' she said, as her jaw hit the floor.

'Yep, just kidding,' I said.

'Take him out of here,' she said to Syl, laughing.

We went back into the cubicle to see Happy-the-doctor. He said that I would have to come back in a few days for a plaster check.

We went home and what a job I had to get round the house with this plaster on my leg. It was a nightmare. It was as if I had a ton weight on my leg, it felt that heavy to walk. Also, my foot felt as though it was going to break through the cast at times. I was in agony.

My foot was giving me so much pain that I couldn't sleep at night because of it. Not only that, I then had the problem of not being able to wear jeans or pants because of it. I had to wear jogging bottoms or shell-suit bottoms as they were easier to put on and take off.

I went back for the plaster check a few days later and was told that I would have to have it on for at least another six weeks.

Having to be in plaster for six weeks caused no end of problems for me. The simplest things like getting around the house from room to room, or getting out of the armchair were now real problems. I would have to really struggle and more than likely I would end up on the floor in a heap. Syl would go potty at me for not asking for help but I felt guilty, thinking that she may have been doing something else and I didn't want to put on her. This led to quite a few arguments, me being so stubborn. I never thought for one minute that it would but it did. Syl asked me once how would I feel if it was her, and she acted like I was doing. She was right but I still felt bad about it; this was a hard thing for me to do, asking for help.

I had an appointment at the hospital for my physiotherapy. I was looking forward to it. I needed to be doing something again but as soon as they saw I was in plaster I was told that I couldn't do any leg exercises until it had been removed. However, I could do some gentle stretching and upper-body work, so that at least was something I could do and do well.

Over the next few weeks I found that little things were starting to go wrong with me. My arms would really ache at the end of the day. It was because I wasn't walking, as such, it was more of a hop, drag, pull, and my arms were doing all the work again instead of my legs. My right leg was very sore and I could not stand on it for very long. Because of this my left leg wasn't getting the exercises that it needed. I tried to do the things that I did before I had the fall, like the exercise of getting on the floor, lying on my back, bending my knees up then slowly taking one leg at a time out to the side. This was not too much of a problem with the left leg but the right one with the plaster on was very hard to work. It would at times just slip and fall or I couldn't bring it back up to the resting position because of the weight of it.

At night the pain was terrible. It seemed to wait till I got into

133

bed then it would start. The right foot would go straight, as if to push the plaster off my leg, and would then start to jump and twist. I seldom got to sleep. Most nights Syl went out and bought the medicine, Night Nurse, to help me and often that didn't even work. I even tried having a few whiskies and a few beers but that was no good either. I just didn't sleep but I had a good time trying.

The day came when the plaster was to be taken off. What a great feeling it was to be rid of it. The first thing I tried to do was to stand up on it but I had no sooner done it than I had to sit down straight away as my ankle gave way.

A doctor took a look at my foot and said that it would take some time to build up the muscle in the ankle. With that I went to the Physiotherapy Department to show them my foot and to find out when I could start back on my exercises. I was told that first I would have to have some treatment on my foot to build it up so that I would be able to put weight on it again.

I was at the Physiotherapy Unit at the hospital for treatment to my ankle and for some light exercises and stretching. They used a machine called a Mega-Pulse on my ankle to help ease the pain but it didn't really work. The pain was just as bad as it had been before. It seemed that any kind of exercises I did on it caused all kinds of pain and discomfort.

I had more X-rays taken to see if there was a problem. There wasn't any sign of anything on the X-rays but the pain was there and I was going through hell, which caused me to be very ratty and irritable. I was so snappy with everyone around me at times, this was a big problem.

I had to have my ankle heavily strapped up again because it was now so weak it kept giving way all the time when I tried to stand. The fall that had caused this had now taken away from me so much, I was now unable to stand or exercise properly. It seemed that everything I had worked so hard to achieve I was now in danger of losing.

I was scared, so very scared, so I started to do the things that I was told not to do, like crawling and using my Zimmer frame. I was told I had to use my wheelchair in the house to rest my foot. Some of the time I did but I wanted to keep on my feet, that was all that really mattered to me. I was doing fine until the old enemy raised its head again: my bladder. It thought it would be a nice time to start to play up again, and how it did.

Back in the November of 1990 a wonderful lady called Eunice came to see me. She was the Incontinence Nurse for the Tameside area. This lady was wonderful. She told me about new sheaths that didn't need to be held on with Micropore as they had their own self-adhesive.

Now these were fantastic things. No more tying myself up like a mummy to stay dry, and no more of the pain that went with it. Well as soon as the trouble started I gave her a ring and she came out to see me to discuss what to do about it. She thought it best if I tried a thing called S.C.T (Self Catheterisation Technique.)

Well, just the thought of it made me wince, but the benefits that it would give me ruled out any thoughts of not giving it a try so I was all for it. She got a catheter out of her bag. It was a long, very thin, clear tube with a green funnel-like piece at one end. As soon as I saw it I thought that I must be mad, but Eunice talked me through it.

There I was sat on the loo with my manhood in one hand, the catheter in the other. I gritted my teeth, gelled the catheter, then slowly inserted it into the top of my you-know-what, and gently pushed. Ha! No pain, no problem! I'd made a mountain out of a molehill.

I looked up and there, peeping round the toilet door, was Vest - Syl.

'There, that didn't hurt did it?' she said with a screwed-up face. She was right, there was no pain, just a strange sort of feeling, a sort of tingling. The thought of doing it was the worst, that was all.

I had emptied my bladder completely for the first time in years and it felt oh, so good. I didn't have that feeling of always wanting to go to the loo and it lasted for quite a long time. Now I had the thing that I'd wanted for so long: something to help me be continent again.

Eunice had gone through with me the ins and outs of everything to do with the hygiene that goes with carrying out self-catheterisation. She spent a long time sorting out the right catheters to use and how to use the gel. She went through it all twice. She also told me not to use the clamp as it did more harm to me than good. She really didn't like that thing at all. I would see a lot of Eunice over the next few years as she kept me in touch with the new things that came out to use.

Syl had been taking driving lessons to help me with the driving. She had had several lessons over the past couple of months and now it was time for her test. She was nervous on the morning but she was also very determined to pass. Hers was the first test of the day and the weather that morning wasn't too good, in fact it was throwing it down with rain.

She came back in just after ten. Her face was down on the floor.

'Never mind, Vest. Not many people pass the first time round. I didn't,' I said, feeling really sorry for her.

'Oh I know! But I did!' she said, with this whooping big grin on her face.

'Well done, Vest! But why the long face?'

'Because you said you would swap the car if I passed first time and I wanted to see your face.'

God, I was gutted. I had forgotten that I had said that. I meant it as a joke. I didn't think she would take it seriously. I loved my car but, true to my word, I took Syl out and we swapped it for a car that suited her. She was over the moon and doing plenty of the driving, which was a nice break for me.

I was going to the Physiotherapy Department at the hospital regularly for treatment on my ankle and to do my exercises, though only on my upper-body. I was starting to use my arms more and more to help me to walk and I had started to drag my right foot behind me. All the bad habits I had once stopped doing, like lifting my legs up to put them on the stairlift, were creeping back in and over the short period I hadn't realised that I was doing it. There were days when my right leg just wouldn't do what I was telling it to do, just like when I first started with MS.

I was now moving my right leg in bed at night with my hands, as there was no feeling in it. There was now just the feeling of pain that the ankle was causing. This was making me feel so low inside and I was hurting with a fear, a fear that my MS was back and this time I couldn't fight it as well as I had in the past.

We needed a break from the day-to-day routine that was all

around us so took the lads to the American Adventure Park in Nottingham again for a day out and they loved it.

The place was packed. It was the May Bank Holiday week-end so you can imagine what it was like. We were walking around the park and I had had a few goes on the rides that I liked with the lads, when we saw Maureen the physio-terrorist with her family and some friends. We went over and let on, and had a quick natter.

We started to all walk in the same direction and carried on the talking about this and that, till we ended up at this ride which was stopped. Gary wanted to go on it, so we let him and off he went till this member of staff shouted, 'Would you like a go?'

Everyone looked round to see whom he was shouting at.

'You! Yes, you in the wheelchair. Would you like a go?'

I really didn't fancy this ride. It looked a bit too daring for me, even though we hadn't seen it in action, so I shouted back to the man, 'I can't get up there!'

The path that led to the ride was that stone-cum-grit type, so I thought that I was safe and I would not have to go on it.

Wrong! The very next thing was that I was being pushed up the path. Not by Syl. No! By the physio-terrorist, Maureen!

'No problem, I'll get you up the path,' she said, as she pushed me through this stone path. She just couldn't wait to get me there. She pushed the wheelchair like it was a plough, just whizzing me through the stones.

When we got to the ride the staff and Maureen, my so-called "friendly" physiotherapist helped me on. I was on the same set of seats as Gary. We were on our own - that tells you something. The rest of the seats on the ride were full. The seats were hard, blue plastic and a bit slippery to say the least. As I had shell-suit bottoms on it was even slippier.

I pulled the safety bar down till it was over my head and on my shoulders. Gary did the same. He was sat about three seats away from me to my right, there were people facing us in one part of the ride, then the rest behind us. Everyone not knowing what to expect (or did they?).

The ride started and we went up and up, and up. Then it just stopped. The people in front of us were looking just how I was feeling: green. Then the ride started to move again, this time the people in front of us moved back to leave a gap. The ride was now in two parts. My heart was on overtime, bumping and beating, going twenty to the dozen. Then the ride really got going. The carriage in front of us raced towards us. Everybody was screaming and holding on for dear life. So were we, and all the people behind us. The ride twisted and turned, then we raced towards the other carriage and came to an abrupt stop.

Gary looked over to me and, with a grin on his face, said, 'Wow! This is really great, dad. I love it!'

I was holding on for dear life with both my arms in the safety bars of the seats next to me and I had them linked in front of me. I was frightened to death, my knuckles were white, I was gripping my hands together that tight.

The ride started up again. I look down and caught a glimpse of the people who had helped me on the ride looking up at me. They looked worried. Me? Well like I say I was scared to death. We did a few more turns to the side then stopped again at the top. I looked down and I could clearly see Syl looking up with her mouth wide open. Then I saw Maureen. She had a panic-stricken look on her face. The ride started to go down. Oh, I was so pleased! I even started to smile again.

People started to get off when it stopped and Maureen brought my wheelchair over to me. A member of staff was with her and he asked me if I'd enjoyed the ride.

'Oh, it was wonderful. A great ride, no problem, mate!' I said to him, tongue in cheek.

'Would you like to stay on for another go, then?' he said smiling.

What! I was in the wheelchair and out of the gate in no time. Maureen and Syl were asking me what it was like. I just said, 'Try it out. It's not that bad. Not that bad at all.'

After that Maureen the physio-terrorist never stopped apologising all day. She said that she would never forget it as long as she lived. Nor will I, Maureen, nor will I.

It was a great day out, we all loved it but it was the last time that I went on any ride again. Well, any ride that I didn't see working first!

We were into June, a lovely time. The weather was quite nice for once. I was still having to have lots of treatment on my ankle at the hospital. Because of this I wasn't doing much exercising on my legs, in fact I was now hardly walking at all and had lost the ability to move the toes on my right foot again.

This was getting me down; so much so that I was taking it out on my legs. I was punching them out of sheer frustration and I was doing it more and more. There was nothing that I could do to help my toes or my legs. The pain in my ankle was so bad it was stopping me from doing the things that I needed to be doing. I was feeling lower and lower in myself and not letting my feelings out. Well, not in the way I should have by talking about them.

Instead I just punched and punched my legs and took it out on them. They were so sore, some days, because of all the punching that they were full of bruises. I had to stop doing certain exercises because of my ankle and it was having a massive effect on my body. Now my back was beginning to suffer. I couldn't do my bridging on the floor to help to strengthen it, as I was sat down all the time, and so I had to do more stretching and reaching to compensate.

It didn't work the same. The bottom part of my back was so weak and giving way, and I was starting to stoop. I looked as though I was about to let someone leapfrog over me, I had that sort of stance.

We were in the house watching TV one night when the phone rang. It was a lady called Mary Bown, from the Manchester branch of the Multiple Sclerosis Society. She asked if we would like to go on holiday with them to Pontins at Prestatyn, Wales for a week. The only problem was that it was that weekend. Someone had dropped out and they had a spare chalet - if we wanted it. We said that we would love it, so she and her husband, Malcolm, came round to see us about it that evening.

We sat there, the four of us, discussing what it was like on the camp. It sounded great for the lads and just what we needed, a break away for a week. We had a really good chat that night and they told us that we only had to take our own food, as the entertainment on the camp was free.

We only had to pay for the chalet and that was at a discount price so we just needed spending money. We decided not to tell the lads and just let it be a surprise for them, one that they would not forget in a long time.

Saturday came. Syl and I had packed the car then told the lads we were going away for a week. We took Edgar, the bird, to Tony's, then we were on our way to Wales for a long overdue holiday. A time to forget our problems for a week.

When we arrived at the holiday camp the lads were so excited. I parked alongside the Multiple Sclerosis Society bus. Mary and Malcolm were there sorting out the chalets for everyone. There were quite a few families there, plus a lot had still not arrived. Some were sorting out their cases, so we introduced ourselves. We unpacked the car. I had to use the wheelchair to get about, except for in the chalet where I used the Zimmer frame.

The lads met some other kids and, just like kids, they went off to see the sights on the camp, leaving us to it. We had a brew and a chat outside to some more of the people who had just arrived, then Syl and I went back into the chalet to finish unpacking.

The chalet was supposed to be a disabled chalet. Well, it had a handrail on the wall in the bathroom, so I suppose that was their idea of a disabled chalet.

We got ready at the night-time to take the lads to see the show in the ballroom and to meet the other people in there. We all sat together, chatting. Some people liked playing bingo, not me. Syl, well she loved playing it. So I had a few drinks with one or two of the other men without the worry of having to drive. The lads did their own thing. There was so much for them to do and so many things going on for them.

The first night when we got back to the chalet we were all drained and went straight to sleep without any problem. First thing in the morning the lads were up early, washed and dressed and waiting to go out to some activity. For the whole of the week we hardly saw them, except at mealtimes and when they needed money. We had a wonderful week and met so many new people. This was the first time, really, that I let myself talk about MS.

Everyone was in the same boat. Everyone had a story to tell about their own experiences, suffering with MS. There was one man there, about my age, that had a sports wheelchair. They are light and can easily be put in the car. It was the type that you could even use on your own if you wanted to drive the car, as the wheels came off it so easily. You could put the whole thing on the front seat. This was the latest thing, then: a far cry from the one that I had.

The independence that would mean was great. I jokingly asked him if he would swap it for my old overweight thing, but surprise, surprise! He said no. Oh well!

We got home and the lads never stopped talking about what had gone on that week. They couldn't wait to go and tell their friends. It was so nice to go away but it was oh so nice to be back home, too.

We picked up Edgar from Tony's on the Sunday morning. The lads always took Edgar upstairs in one of the bedrooms so he could have a fly round while they played on the computer. There was no room to let Edgar fly downstairs. It wasn't safe for him because of the things hanging from the beams. Syl had taught him to whistle the Laurel and Hardy tune and he always did it when I was walking past his cage on my frame. Off he would whistle, with his head bobbing up and down as he went. I had just had a good week's rest, well sort of. I was refuelled, fit, and raring to go, and now I was back home it was back to getting myself right again.

Chapter Thirteen

I was feeling fit and full of new-found enthusiasm after the holiday, so I started to get down to some serious work on myself. I felt good inside, so good that it seemed everything I did I did with ease, and now I was so keen to prove to myself that I could do most things. The amount of work I got through in a day was fantastic but the pain my ankle was giving me still stopped me from using my Zimmer frame.

I couldn't stand on my ankle and I couldn't feel my right leg at all from the knee down. All I could feel was the pain of my foot twisting inwards. It was stopping me from doing so much and it would play up at the most inopportune times, like just when I was going to eat. The twisting would start and I would have to stop eating to hold my leg still or to rub it. I even started to carry some Fiery-Jack ointment to rub on it but even that didn't shift the pain.

It seemed that nothing I did helped ease the pain. The one thing that did seem to work, though, was the machine at the Physiotherapy Department. I had treatment there twice a week and felt I was now getting somewhere, as I had been before I had the fall.

Then one day I went for physiotherapy and was told that they were short-staffed and I could no longer be treated there.

Well, I had been here before: just as I was doing well the carpet was pulled from under me. What's new?

That meant I had no equipment to use and I would have to make do with the things I used at home. How often things like this happen in life. One minute things are going great, then bang! You're back to square one. Well I was.

The trouble with me was that to get to square two I had to go through some doors. Just as I was going through those doors, though, and doing well, they would be slammed in my face. Now it was a case of having to get over that and start to do the best I could with the things that were around me.

"If only!" I don't know how many times I've said that: "If only I had done this." or "If only they had given me a few more weeks!".

Well it was "pick yourself up" time again so I did. I was doing all the exercises I could and Syl and the lads would help me, too. We are a great team. But I still had a terrible problem with the ankle; I needed help so I asked for some.

I was given some physiotherapy at home by Maureen the physio-terrorist. She brought the Mega Pulse machine and used that on my ankle for a few weeks to see if it would help and it did. Also, I was also given some tablets to ease the pain by Doctor Walton. They were called Carbamazepine and they seemed to work for a while. The pain wasn't as bad. I now had some small semblance of peace from pain for a few hours a day. Then it was back to square one again. The pain would come back and this time with a vengeance.

I was asked to go into the Y.D.U. (Young Disabled Unit) at Rochdale by Doctor Walton. I would have a course of intense physiotherapy while I was in there and it would also give Doctor Walton the chance to take a good look at me over a few weeks. I was all for this, even though it meant being away from home for those few weeks while I was in the unit. I could come home each weekend, though, so I couldn't wait to get started and get back on the road to standing and using my frame again.

In the September of 1991 I went into the Y.D.U. at Birch Hill Hospital in Rochdale for some intense physiotherapy. I had my own room and was able to look after myself, as I had been asked when I arrived just what I could and could not do. There was a pool table there and plenty of board games and things to use to keep us amused. In the corridor just near the physiotherapy room there was a set of parallel bars, the very thing that I wanted to use most of all.

In the unit there was a room for occupational therapy (O.T.) where we had to go and do different things each day. The Occupational Therapists would ask questions about how I managed around the house, getting about outside, and dressing and eating; anything that involved my independence.

It was great. I was having physiotherapy twice daily and

often I knocked on the door of the physiotherapy room when it was quiet and did a bit more. They couldn't believe how I didn't fatigue easily and how much I would do each time I went in there.

I soon started to get into a good routine. I was using the parallel bars quite a lot, with the physiotherapists there. Then, when there was nobody around, I would go back and walk on them on my own. The only thing was that I was still dragging my right leg. My right knee now just wouldn't straighten and I couldn't put any sort of weight through it. One of the physiotherapists there, after the first week, had got me to stand and walk with a Zimmer frame again and quite well too. I went home after the first week feeling great and able to get about the house without too much help.

That first Saturday back home I took us all to see Syl's mum, Edie, who was very ill and bedridden. She was suffering from emphysema. She had fought this for many years and had been in and out of hospital, which had taken its toll on her. Syl was at her wits' end with worry and it was showing. She was having to cope with her mum's illness and me being in hospital at the same time.

Syl was putting on a brave face, but I knew her. She was hurting so very, very much. She had a great relationship with her mum and her family. We spent as much time as we could with Edie but we also had to let her get her rest.

Syl's eyes would glaze over with tears when she saw her mum fighting for breath. The love she had for her was clear for all to see. These were hard days for everyone in the family.

I went back into the Y.D.U. on the Monday and got back into the things that I had been doing before. I had the weekend at home but I couldn't settle down and concentrate on the things that I was supposed to be doing. I was too busy thinking of how things were at home. I phoned Syl every day to see how she was and to find out how Edie was doing. Syl was talkative but not as much as usual.

This made me feel something that I had not felt before - stress. It was starting to have an effect on my MS. I got to the Thursday and I was asked to have a go on some crutches, which I tried but only managed a few steps. This was so good, though. I was once again moving in the right direction. Later that same day I did manage to walk quite a distance on my frame and that cheered me up no end.

I had decided that I would have to call it a day and go home as things were worsening with Syl's mum. I was all prepared to go home for good when Doctor Walton asked me to stay for another week as I was really doing well. But there was no way that I could. I needed to be with Syl at this time. Doctor Walton understood the situation I was in, so I left on the Friday and made an appointment to see her at her clinic at Tameside the following month.

It had been good in the Y.D.U. I had really benefited from going in there and having the intense physiotherapy. I also enjoyed the chance to help out with some of the other patients who were there. I did things like helping patients to eat their food when they couldn't feed themselves; I helped someone by reading them a paper and generally helped by just being around and talking to people. Now that's something I'm very good at, talking.

I was now back at home and soon in the old routine of things again. I was up at seven o'clock to do my exercises, let the lads out for school and then Syl would walk over for the papers. When she came back in I had a drink waiting for her, then after settling down for an hour we would go and do what shopping had to be done that day.

This was our daily routine but it was slowly changing. Edie was by now very ill and we would go to see her every day. I would stay in the living room talking to Syl's dad about football and this and that, while Syl would be in the bedroom with some of her sisters looking after Edie.

She was the most wonderful woman. She'd had sixteen children and, besides looking after them, had always worked. She was only a small lady but so, so strong in her personality and in body. From day one of meeting her she treated me like a son and was always there when and if I needed her. You could take your problems to her and she could always find the answer.

She had a long, hard fight with her illness, which at times was very severe, yet she always had a smile on her face. She was a fighter, a fighter that would never let go. But then, on the 13th of October, Edie passed away.

Syl received a phone call in the early hours of the morning from her elder sister, Linda, to tell her that her mum had passed away. I could hear her crying downstairs in the kitchen as they spoke on the phone.

After a short while Syl came back into the bedroom. She

was crying uncontrollably. I burst into tears myself as I held her as close to me as I could. I, too, had just lost someone who I thought the world of: Edie.

This caused Syl to be ill for a long time. Her grief was so bad that she had to have treatment from the doctor to help her through it. I was, for once, helpless to do anything to help her. All I could do was be there for her to talk to, and help her as much as I could - whatever it took.

But then, right on cue, my MS started to play up. As soon as I saw Syl feeling low and crying all the time, I was at a loss at how to help her. I was hurting inside at not being able to reach her and comfort her, as I normally could.

I started to get these strange effects around my body. It would either be my legs that just didn't work, or my hands that would start to go into spasm. It would go as quickly as it came but while it was there it scared the life out of me, I can tell you. In another sense it made me see that stress was playing a huge part in some of the things that went wrong with me.

The next few weeks saw Syl not wanting to go out much. She found it hard to talk to people as she would just burst into tears if anyone spoke to her. She had many friends and it seemed that every time that she saw them they would ask about her mum.

I was doing the best I could to help her to take her mind off things throughout the day. I would take us to the pictures and then for a meal out - well it was a kebab on the B&Q car park. I'm such a romantic. It seemed to work, though, because by Christmas, Syl was getting to find herself again. Even though she had gone through so much grief.

God Bless, Edie (Queen).

Christmas was upon us and, as usual for us, was very busy. That helped Syl to take her mind off things for a while. She was still grieving for her mum and some nights would cry herself to sleep; other nights we would just lay there talking about Edie.

Somehow we got through the festive period. It wasn't easy but we got there without too much of a problem. New Year was the same. Instead of looking forwards to the year ahead, as we normally did, we just decided to let it happen. I had to see Doctor Walton at Tameside hospital. I was put on a course of steroid injections to help me as my MS, because of the stress, had started to play up in its usual way.

I had been doing so well with all my exercising and I was physically well in all other departments. My ankle, though, just wouldn't respond to any sort of treatment I was given. I was once again suffering through it, so I was back off my feet and using the wheelchair in the house, as well as outside.

This was something that I had fought so hard to get out of having to do, but the use of the Zimmer frame in the house was becoming less and less. It was now just a case of a quick walk from the stairlift to the kitchen where my wheelchair would be. Even then I would fall fifty per cent of the time and end up crawling the rest of the way.

This used to make me mad. I couldn't come to terms with the fact that I had to go back to using the wheelchair in the house again. I had worked so hard to stay on my feet and now, through that stupid fall on the ramp, I had to try again. This time I knew in my heart that there was very little chance of my ever walking again, unless there was a miracle cure, and I couldn't see that happening.

I then found that I seemed to be checking the papers more and listening to the news for anything that had to do with MS. This wasn't my style. I was usually the one who said, "Sod the news. I will make my own!" and got on with it.

It took me a few weeks to sort myself out and get back to the old me, the one who fought every inch of the way, the one that had a smile on his face and didn't take "no" for an answer where MS was concerned.

Because of not getting about as well as I had been, and my general state of health, the toilet and bathroom in the house were causing me some problems again. Social Services came up with the idea of a wheel-in, wheel-out shower. This was a great idea. I was all for this as I was really struggling now to get in and out of the bath.

We had people in measuring up and coming up with different ideas until we settled on one and got the go-ahead to start the work. Besides all this happening, Maureen the physio-terrorist brought a standing frame for me to use in the house to help strengthen my legs. I looked like Hannibal Lecter from the film, The Silence of the Lambs. All I needed was the mask.

The frame was smashing, it did a great job for me. It was a frame that I had to get into standing up. It had a bar that went across my knees, and a bar about chest height with a strap attached to it that went around my bottom. This was great! It enabled me to stand up without holding on to anything. It did a fantastic job for me but I could only stand in it for short periods as my ankle would start to do its twisting and turning on me.

I would stand up several times each day and even watched TV whilst standing in it. It helped with my digestion and other things, but best of all, to me, was how nice it was to have a cup of coffee standing up, watching TV, without having to hold on to something for support.

The things I was now able to do using the frame were great: having a drink, a sandwich at dinnertime, reading the paper, standing with my hands in my pockets, having a chat. Wow! This was magic, pure luxury to me.

The only thing that I couldn't do, and had wanted to for so long, was to stand at the toilet like I used to and have a pee. Oh, the pleasure that would bring! But what a lot of trouble we would have, getting the frame up the stairs, or in the pub toilets. I think that I might have been noticed!

The frame gave me back so much; it even helped my bladder. Instead of sitting all the time I now had a proper stance once again and I felt so much more alive.

I was doing well again and felt good. Everything was going to plan. I even gave up smoking - well it was pushed on me by Syl. She wouldn't let me smoke in the house because every time I had a cigarette I would get a burning feeling in my legs. So she said, in her infinite wisdom, that she couldn't see me suffer like that over a cigarette and made me go to my car or on the drive to smoke. She was right. I was making myself ill, the pain I got after I had a cigarette. It was bad, so I called it a day and just stopped, on the day I had to pick up Tony and Jane's new baby, Kate, from hospital.

Maureen, the physio-terrorist was treating me at home and we were doing quite well. Then, just as always when I'm on the up, slam! Another door closes. Maureen had to stop treating me because of cutbacks in the services, so it was back to that old familiar square one again. I will get off it one day!

It was now back down to me. I never stopped doing things, anyway, as I had too much to lose and so much to gain. I was on the floor working hard to get myself right. I was there every day, two, three, four times a day, doing everything that I had been shown and a few things I just threw in at the time. And I threw in some really good exercise of my own that I'd made up through the years.

I had reached April and I was now starting to feel low in myself again. It seemed that I was getting nowhere with the things I was doing. I was doing plenty of work on myself but I was getting worse. I went to see Doctor Walton about my right knee giving way every time I put any sort of weight on it. She got me a knee-brace to see if that would be of help. This seemed to do the trick for a while but, as always, there was a problem. Every time I wanted to drive the car I would have to take it off till I got to the other end, then put it back on. This was really awkward at times so I stopped using it. Maureen the physio-terrorist had written to my old workmates and the local branch of the Multiple Sclerosis Society about getting me a new wheelchair and, thanks to her, they did just that. They raised enough money to buy me a new wheelchair, one of those super-duper, sporty types, which only weighed just over twenty pounds.

This made my life so much easier. I could get around the house without any problems and I was zooming to the shops with ease. I could also go out on my own, now, as the wheels came off and I could put the wheelchair on the passenger seat of my car. I was like Billy Whiz, doing wheelies so easily for once. Right then I didn't mind having to be in a wheelchair, as this one really was a sporty-looking thing. But, just like me, I pushed it and started having problems with my arms and hands, which became very, very sore.

My right hand would go into a sort of spasm, specially when I had been out shopping and my arms would ache something chronic. I never wanted anyone to push me in my wheelchair, I wanted to do it all myself. I wanted to be "Mr. Independent". I thought it was just a matter of getting used to the new wheelchair and then everything would be as normal and the pain would go. Wrong! The pain was there most of the time. I couldn't get rid of it, no matter how many painkillers I took.

I cut down on going out and let Syl push me from time to time when we did. This worked, the pain got better and the spasms went away so now I had to watch just what I was doing and not go overdoing it anymore.

Our son, Gary had to go into hospital for an operation to sort out the squint in his eye and everyone was on edge. My nerves were not too clever, to say the least, and Syl was just as bad, if not worse, with worry. He had already been in hospital twice before for the same operation and it had not worked so this was the last chance for him. He was as bright as a button and so brave. After all that he had been through he was putting on this brave face.

We took him into a different hospital this time - Oldham Infirmary - and he had the operation. It all went wonderfully. Gary's doctor said that the operation was a great success and his eye would be perfect from now on. All the time Gary was in hospital my MS went crazy. There was nothing I could do about it; the stress just made it happen. This was now part and parcel of my MS, the stress factor. So we decided that it was time we had a holiday, as we all needed one, so Syl and I booked to go away with the Multiple Sclerosis Society to Wales again, back to Pontins.

We told the lads that we were going back to Pontins for a week's holiday and they couldn't wait. Over the coming weeks they talked of nothing else but the holiday and what they were going to do when they got there. They, like us, needed this break, a break from the old routine of everyday life and it didn't take long till the morning of the holiday arrived.

Syl and I packed the car, as before. This time, with the lads' help, we were ready in no time. We locked the house up, dropped Edgar off at Tony's then we were off.

When we got there we even had the same chalet as the year before. We knew everyone from the Multiple Sclerosis Society this time as we were branch members and went to the meetings and did the collections with them. The lads soon settled in, as did we all. It was as if we hadn't been away. Everything was the same as before, except this time I was having a hard time getting round the chalet in my wheelchair.

This time I had to crawl down the passageway to get in the bathroom and we couldn't use the bedroom we used the year before, as I couldn't get the new wheelchair through the door that led to them, so we had to use the sofa-bed in the living area.

It was a great week. We saw and did plenty and I was so glad I had my new sports wheelchair, it made a big difference.

There was a train, well a tractor, that pulled some carriages round the camp and it was full of mums and dads with their kids.

In the back carriage were some people from our party so I

raced up to them and grabbed hold of a bar so the train could pull me along in my wheelchair. Big, big mistake! The train was only going slowly (thank God) when it went over one of those humps that slow the cars down, and who didn't see the thing until, whoops, I went over  it at speed. I was like something out of a circus. I just managed to stay in my chair - just. I was scared to death.

The kids on the train thought that I was brilliant. What a total wart I was! I wheeled myself out of sight and just slumped back in my chair thinking, "That's what you get for showing off, pal!".

By the end of the week my knees were sore because of all the crawling I had to do in the chalet to get into the toilet. I was having to get my wheelchair as close as possible to the living room door that led to the toilet. Then I'd drop to my knees, crawl down the passage, which was about twelve to fifteen feet long, and into the bathroom where I would have to then pull myself onto the loo.

Then there was the problem of getting my trousers off and using the loo. This was very difficult at times as there were no bars to hold on to, just the towel rail, which, after the first day, was pulled off the wall "accidentally".

It was then a case of getting up to get my pants pulled up then crawl back to my wheelchair. After a day of doing this I didn't really need to do many exercises. I was doing enough just doing this.

Don't get me wrong! The holiday was great but it would have been a lot better if large holiday camps like this paid a little more attention to the needs of their disabled guests.

By the end of the week I could have done with another holiday to revive myself from this one! We'd had a great week, the lads had had a great time, but all the crawling took it out of me and for the next couple of weeks when we got back home I didn't really go out, only fishing the odd time with our Tony.

In August I had to have another course of steroids to help me. I wasn't at my best and I wasn't doing any walking at all now because my arms just couldn't hold me up. It seemed that all my body was aching because of trying to do too much. My arms and shoulders were the worst through trying to hold myself up on my Zimmer frame. My ankle was, as usual, giving me hell, but this time my right foot felt as though someone was trying to break it off, especially at night in bed.

I sometimes thought that someone was trying to pull me out of bed, the spasm I was getting in it was so severe. I was finding now that I couldn't bend my right leg. At times it would just shoot out straight and go very rigid and totally stiff.

Syl would help me as much as she could with it. I would lie on my stomach and she would have to bend my heel up to my bottom several times to ease it. This did the trick for a short while, then it would come back and we would have to do it all over again. We were lucky to get any sleep some nights through it all, as it only took the slightest movements, sometimes, to trigger it off.

I started to do one of my super-duper workout routines to music every morning, to get myself into really top shape again. I wouldn't mind but I was already fit anyway and working hard on my exercises. I just wanted to do more.

With all my good intentions of doing more to get better quicker, I then caused another problem for myself. I cut the base of my spine doing sit-ups on the hard floor. This caused all kinds of problems for me. For one, I had to stop doing any exercises which involved lying on my back for a few weeks.

Once again I had tried too hard and made things worse for myself. I could never learn to do things in moderation. I always had to overdo it and rush things. I just wanted to be well and get on my feet again so this was why I put everything I had into everything I did. I just had to achieve things.

But, because of overdoing things, I now had to wait a few weeks before I could get on the floor and get stuck into getting myself right again. So, in the meantime, I did plenty of wheelchair workouts and standing in my frame, anything to keep me active.

Chapter Fourteen

November came and my legs were very sore. I had to increase the Carbamazepine tablets I was taking to help with this terrible nerve pain I was getting. And now through not being able to get on the floor and do the exercises, which had been helping me, my temper was really out of control. I was so fed up with myself. I was putting lots of effort into everything I did but I still had nothing to show for it, except this terrible pain and an empty feeling inside.

I was running scared. Scared that I was losing my battle with MS, because now my arms were getting so bad that at night when I lay in bed resting they would jump and twitch for no reason. I lay in bed each night so scared that I couldn't sleep.

I was frightened and didn't know what to do for the best, till one day Syl told me she had made an appointment for me to see Doctor Hussein. This guy is great. I've always got on well with him in the past and found him so easy to speak to. On the day of the appointment we went into his room and, as usual, he was very cheery and full of smiles. He put us at ease the minute we walked in.

I told him I had pains in my arms and that at times they went into a sort of spasm. Right away I asked him if it was my MS playing up again. He took hold of my arm and touched my elbow, I almost went into orbit, it hurt that much. He smiled at me and told me I had tennis elbow. Well, I wanted to run around in circles shouting at the top of my voice but my legs wouldn't, so I just gave this huge sigh of relief. Oh what a feeling! To be told that it was tennis elbow and not what I had imagined.

From then on I was on cloud nine. I was feeling wonderful again and the smile was back on my face. It was my fault, all the pain.

I had caused it overdoing it with the weights and pushing myself to the limit in my wheelchair when I shouldn't have been. All this trying to get myself better was, at times, making me worse. I just couldn't find a middle ground.

There was going to be lots of work done in the house soon. The date for the new wheel-in, wheel-out shower had been sorted out and things would be a lot easier for me. It was going to be fantastic. Also, we were to have a new stairlift, as the old one kept breaking down all the time. There's nothing worse than when you get on your lift to go to bed and it just won't work. This happened many, many times. We would phone the emergency number but they couldn't do anything until the morning, so it was either sleep on the floor, or do the "Krypton Factor impression" and get up the stairs that way.

Now, the "Krypton Factor impression", as we called it, was to lie on my back on the stairs, then hold on to the banister from beneath, with Syl holding my legs. Then I would pull myself up, arm over arm, until I reached the top. Now that was hard work. Good fun going down but very hard work going up. When you have to do that several times a month, though, because the lift doesn't work, you can see why we needed the new stairlift.

Our Occupational Therapist, Kath "cherry lips" Higgerson, came to sort it out. She had the shower room organised for us. Now she was doing the organising of the stairlift, too, and it went well, with no problems for once. The new stairlift was slower than the one they'd taken out.

Getting from bottom to the top took ages. I could sing the whole of King of the Road before it reached the top of the stairs, that's how slow it was. But it did the trick. It got me to where I needed to go and that's all that mattered, and I love to sing that song anyway!

Now everything in the house was going to be OK I just needed to work on me, and work on me is what I would do.

December came and, as usual, we were very busy getting ready for Christmas and New Year. All the shopping had been done and there wasn't a lot left to do now but enjoy it and we were going to do that. Tony, Jane and the girls came to visit us just before Christmas and Tony and I had a few beers in the house. I was well in myself and in very good spirits. In fact, to be honest, I was more like my old self again. I had tried a few times over the past weeks to get myself walking again but I wasn't too good at it. I wanted to be back on my feet again for Christmas, so I was trying and trying to walk using the Zimmer frame but to no avail.

I was on my stairlift coming down from the toilet when I thought, "Sod it, I'll try again while Tony and Jane are here and show them just how good I could do things again.".

Well I'd had a few too many beers and when I got off my stairlift and tried to walk into the kitchen with my Zimmer frame I fell. Tony came rushing out to see what had happened and saw me sprawled out on the floor.

'Did you fall?' he said, as he leaned over to help me.

'Oh, no, Toe! I'm just trying to break this bar of chocolate in my back pocket.'

Syl and Jane came in to see what was going on and started laughing at Tony and me struggling to get up. They all helped me into my wheelchair and, as usual, we had a good laugh about it all.

There I was, once again, trying to run before I could even crawl again. That was me - I had to keep on doing the things that kept the light burning inside me, whatever the consequences.

I was feeling strong again. The injection that Doctor Hussein had given me in my elbow had worked wonders. The pains had gone and I was feeling fine, so I thought that it would be OK to go and do all the things that had caused it in the first place. I just never learned, I was my own worst enemy. I went right back and carried on doing all the same things again. It was Christmas and I thought that gave me the right to go over the top with the food and drink. The weight piled on, and on, and on, just as it had before. I was back to square one again: out of shape and feeling low in myself. I was on a diet, again, for the New Year.

1993 started with me on this strict diet and trying to get back into the swing of things. I was having a real struggle with my legs now. They were very stiff and tightly closed together. At times I could hardly open them, so I used to sit on the floor, or in my wheelchair, with my legs crossed. Syl said that when I sat like that I looked like Buddha. I suppose I did, especially as I was so overweight as well. But I didn't care, it did the job I wanted, it took the stiffness away for a while.

Over the next few weeks everything started going OK. I was getting around the house better in my wheelchair, as my arms were so much better. But, more importantly, I think it was because I had stopped moaning about using the wheelchair in the house and had accepted the fact that this was now the way it was going to have to be. It had taken me a long time getting there but I got there in the end and it was so much easier now all the moaning and the, "I hate this chair" had stopped.

It was February and, just my luck, I got another water infection. Now there's a surprise! But this one was a bad one. I had a course of strong antibiotics and it went almost as quickly as it came.

Syl and I were talking and she remembered the time that I was rushed into hospital. I had these terrible pains in my stomach and side and I couldn't bear to touch them as they were so sore. Syl telephoned for the doctor to come out as I was getting worse and couldn't stop shaking and trembling. I was in bed and needed the toilet, so Syl said she would get me a bottle to use. I wouldn't do that. The toilet was only just outside the bedroom door, so I tried to get there under my own steam and started to crawl. The pain was unbelievable. My kidneys were on fire, or so I thought. My arms, knees, everything hurt. I was in so much pain but I still had to do it my way. And I still failed.

I ended up just sprawled on the floor of the landing, making it even harder for Syl. Instead of me doing the right thing and staying in bed and using a bottle, like she had asked me to, I had done all this and now she had to somehow get me back to bed.

As she was doing her "Wilma Flintstone" routine - pulling me across the floor by my arms - the doorbell rang. It was Doctor Hussein. He took a look at me there on the floor, shook his head, said a few words to Syl, then helped her get me into bed. He gave me a good examination then rang for the ambulance.

I don't remember anything else except going in the ambulance and waking up in hospital. When I awoke I was on top of the bed, with just a sheet over me, and totally naked. I was really embarrassed at being in the "nuddy".

There was a nurse at the side of me. She told me where I was and that I had had a very rough night. She said I was very poorly, had a high temperature and they were trying to get it down. That was why I had no clothes on, only a sheet. She told me there was no pacifying me in the night as I kept on asking for my vest, but I didn't have one with me when I'd been admitted.

I just laughed and she gave me a very strange stare.

'"Vest" is my wife, Syl! That's what I call her,' I said.

She just went, 'Oh, isn't that nice!'

I felt such a wally. Everyone on the ward knew all about it after that. When Syl walked on the ward the Sister, who was at the bed next to mine, said to me really loudly, so everyone could hear, 'Here's your Vest!'

I was in hospital for a few days. I had tests done and all the usual things but mostly I had bed rest. When I was allowed home I had to stay in bed for a few more days.

It seemed that there was one thing I could always count on and that was a water infection.

I started to mess about with the weights again to build myself back up but I overdid it and got what I deserved, a pain in my shoulders and arms. I had to have ultrasound treatment on them, which was done by Barbara, one of Maureen the physio-terrorist's colleagues. It worked well. I was feeling great again after a few treatments but I was told by Barbara not to use the weights again for a good while as I was doing more damage than good.

By this time I was really fit again. The weight I had put on was now almost gone so I thought why not try to use the Zimmer frame again, so I did. I walked (well hopped) from the kitchen to the stairlift and back. I felt so good at being able to do this again I thought why not carry on doing it a few times each day, so I did.

Everything was going great until the day I had one of my super workouts. I had done lots of work on the floor exercising, then tried to walk to the stairlift. I started out with no problems then I got one of the spasms in my leg. That made it go stiff and I fell onto the coffee table and tumbled over the other side. The table was fine but I broke my ribs, so that put paid to my walking again for a while.

From then on it seemed that whatever I did went wrong, and oh, how it all went wrong. My MS started to play up. My legs were now starting to go stiff when I transferred from my easy chair to wheelchair, or to the stairlift, or into or out of the car, which made it very difficult at times. This always seemed to happen just when somebody was walking past.

Well, some of the faces on people when this happened. The poor person wouldn't know where to look. There I was, as stiff as a board, trying to loosen off my legs, and Syl trying to bend them at the same time. It was crazy and a real struggle.

Then I would start to lose my rag with myself because it made me so embarrassed when it happened. Syl would tell me to calm down as I was making it worse, but I never could. It always ended in the same way: after all the struggling and fighting with them, they would just loosen off on their own.

Then the other problem with them would start. I would put my feet on the footrest of the wheelchair, or the floor, and the "bops" would start. I would go into my Elvis impression. My legs, mostly my right, would jump up and down. I could put all my weight through them to stop it but they never would. In the end it was down to Syl to sit on my knee or to press down as hard as she could, and she could.

The MS was now starting to shape my life in a big way. All the little things that would once happen at different times, and in different ways, were now things that were happening all the time, and all at once. The things we had to put up with and do just to go to the shops, or to visit someone, were crazy at times. If only they knew!

It was that time in the year when the lads needed a break from the norm. A day out was called for, so we took them to Wales for the day so they could let off some steam and have a go on the rides at the fun-fair.

We had a great day out. The lads really let off all their steam. They were playing with a ball we had got them and I was watching them, kicking it to each other. The ball, at one stage, rolled out of their way and this man kicked it back to them. I was so envious of that man. I so wanted to play ball with my sons I would have given anything to do so. When we got home we were all shattered. It had been a great family day out and for once my MS wasn't too bad. It behaved and let me enjoy the day with my family. It was so good to forget all the everyday problems for once.

After every good day it seemed that I had to pay the price with a bad one. I did. I got a kidney infection, so I phoned Eunice to see if she could help me to find out why these things kept on happening to me. She went though my catheterising technique to see if I was doing it correctly. I was, and I was so strict about my hygiene and the things that went with it, so that wasn't the problem.

She left me some bladder washes to do myself. No big deal, just a bag with some special water in it. It was easy to do, just the same sort of thing as using the catheter. You insert the catheter, then the bag with the wash on the other end. The water then goes down the catheter and into your bladder to wash it out. Then, after the bag has emptied, you take the catheter out and throw it all away - simple.

I had a few weeks of everything going great. I even got the Zimmer frame out and started to do my hop-walking again. Then came August and I got yet another water infection. This was the third in five months and it took it out of me.

I was drained and not in any real shape to do anything about it. The pains from it were terrible and the stiffness I was also getting was incredible. I just didn't know what I was doing to cause it to happen. I was going backwards again and starting to blame myself for all my problems. I would go into the toilet, look at myself in the mirror and cry. I couldn't bear it. The MS was getting to me and I couldn't tell anyone how I felt because I felt I had to deal with it. I had to keep this to myself and keep on going as well as I could. I'd just wash my face and carry on as normal.

The year had been full of so many ups and downs and I had gone through so many different mood swings, it didn't seem possible that I was letting it get to me in this way. All the pains in my legs one minute, then the next, water infections. It seemed that I couldn't get myself well. Now the tennis elbow had started to play up and this always stopped me from doing so much as I was so dependent on my arms to do everything.

I made an appointment to see Doctor Hussein to have it sorted out and he gave me a cortisone injection. Once again I would be OK for another few months or so. While I was there I came so near to telling him how I was feeling emotionally, but I just couldn't bring myself to say the words. I was scared and falling apart inside.

So I buried myself in my exercises and just got on with it. I was doing plenty of loosening exercises to help with the stiffness in my legs. They didn't seem to do much good so I went to see Doctor Walton at the hospital. We had a good chat and I told her about all the water infections I had been having.

She had X-rays taken of my bladder and blood tests to see what the problem was, plus she also upped the amount of Baclofen loosening tablets I was taking to help with the stiffness. Now the only trouble was that these tablets, although they did a good job on my legs, loosened my upper-body and on days I would be like a limp rag doll. I had to juggle the dosage about until I got it right. It took time but in the end I got it correct. The stiffness wasn't so bad but the pain was still there in my legs and it seemed that nothing was going to get rid of it.

The X-rays came back clear and there was no sign of anything wrong, or of any problems with my bladder. So, why all the infections? I made sure from that day that I double-washed the catheters when I took them out of their bags. Then after using them I threw them away, just as I was told to do. But, then again, I had always done that from day one. I even tried to cut down on the number of times I used the catheters but that didn't work so I was back to square one.

There were some things going well for me, though. Everything wasn't all doom and gloom. Tony and I were doing lots of fishing and getting out and about and I was getting out every once in a while for a pint with my other brothers-in-law, so I wasn't that bad really.

There was a family night we had when the big World Wrestling Federation matches were on Sky TV. They were great nights, the whole family loved them. Well, everyone but Gary. He was growing up now and didn't want to be seen enjoying things like that. I could see him pretending not to be interested, yet there he was with his sweets in his hand, totally fixed to the action.

The lads were changing now they were both at secondary school and doing well in their work. I used to sit back and just watch the things they did - mostly arguing over their computer. I would teach them how to play cards or dominoes and we would sit there on the carpet playing for ages.

There were times when we would be playing cards on the floor and I wished that I could jump to my feet and say, "Right, let's go outside and have a game of football.".

But it just couldn't be. So I carried on as normal, playing cards with this burning feeling inside of me, and a wish that maybe, just maybe, one day things would change. I'd be able to walk once again and do some of the things I used to do with my family.

One day!

Chapter Fifteen

The lads were growing up so fast. One minute they were little lads playing with their toys without a care in the world; the next they were young men with all the pressures that teenagers experience.

Their temperaments were changing, too. Gary thought that because he was older and bigger in size it entitled him to boss Adam about. Whatever Adam did it was wrong, from the things he was playing with to the clothes that he wore. Gary would say that he was a baby or that he should get a life.

Adam was no saint, either. He would, for no reason, start trouble with Gary over the slightest thing. This led to some very tough arguments in the house and they always seemed blow up so quickly and without any real reason. They also always seemed to be upstairs and out of my way, so when this happened, and it happened each and every day, Syl was the one who had to deal with them, which used to send me potty. Just the fact of not being able to get up the stairs in time to sort it out used to hurt me so much. This was my job, a father's job, sorting out the little differences that happened in families, but by the time I got up there on my stairlift they would have either half-killed each other, or Syl had sorted it out.

There were times when arguments were going on at the top of the stairs and I would rush to my stairlift and transfer on to it from my wheelchair, all the time ranting and raving. I would then start to go up the stairs on the "Orient Express", jerking and twisting trying to make it go faster and all the time I would be saying, as I was going up, 'Just you wait till I get there.'

What a joke! The lads could have had a game of cards and a three-course lunch before I got there on that chair. They would stand there at the top of the stairs looking down at me "racing" towards them at an unbelievable speed and I'd see one of them snigger so I'd say, 'Oh, yes. Funny is it? Well, we'll see who's laughing in a minute.'

I must have looked a right prat doing all this, but best of all was, they would stand there and wait till I got to the top. Then when I finally reached them I would say, 'OK, what was that all about, then?'

Just the opposite of what I was going to do when I got on the lift.

The lads would start then with Gary shouting, 'It's him he's being soft.'

Then Adam would scream out his side. 'He don't like it 'cos I beat him at a game.'

There were times when I could have killed the person who invented computer games. Then again it was our fault for buying them in the first place. Believe it or not I loved those days. It was so easy to sort out, it was a case of saying, "Right you two, you're grounded for a week.".

Or Syl would shout out, "Send them to bed.".

They were now teenagers and wanted to be treated like teenagers but they didn't act it at times. We never asked much of them but it seemed that the things we did ask them to do were too much trouble. We love our lads and think the world of them but at times we just didn't like them much!

Yet another year was drawing to a close and this year was very difficult to buy for the lads. How easy it used to be. When they played with certain toys we could go to the toy shop and get them, now they were into clothes and music, but not just any old clothes. Oh, no they now had to have "Designer Labels" on them. And the music they liked was something else!

Gary liked rap music; the sort that should have a "C" in front of it. Adam liked the sort that was in the charts but that was no use to us. We didn't know one band from the next, so it was down to "I-Spy Syl", to snoop around their rooms for clues.

By the time Christmas was upon us we had sorted out the right things for each of them, plus one or two surprises. Once again we had a great Christmas and everyone got what they wanted. It had been hard that year but as usual we got through it. We just hoped for some better luck the following year and for thing to improve on the health-front for me. But that wasn't to be.

1994 started off with me still in lots of pain with my right leg. There seemed to be no escape from it. Just as I was about to settle down for the night it would start its twisting and turning but whereas once I could walk it off, I now had to just suffer and get on with it. And besides all the sleepless nights and constant pain I was having, my MS went into another gear.

It was now affecting me more and more and there was very little I could do to stop it. I couldn't wriggle my toes or even move my leg. Nothing worked, now. I had lost everything that once worked in my right leg and now the left one was going the same way. It was all through the lack of movement and constant sitting down in my wheelchair I was forced to do. I needed to be more mobile and active. This was my only way to fight back.

I used the standing frame to strengthen my legs for up to three hours a day, or for as long as my right ankle would let me. The ramp was too icy to walk down so I couldn't use that as parallel bars as I once had done, and using the Zimmer frame was putting too much pressure on my arms. Crawling was out, as it, too, was causing too much trouble, so all I had left was the wheelchair to use and I had to use it all the time or sit in the armchair and look out of the window.

I was lent a TENS pain-relieving machine to see if that would help ease any of the pains I was having. Well, a lot of it was self-inflicted through overdoing it and the rest was down to the MS and nerve pain.

I tried the TENS on my shoulder and it seemed to work. Great. So, Syl wired it up to my elbow to see if it would help that. Wow! What a mistake! I turned it on and the whole of my arm became distorted. I couldn't turn it off as my arm was almost up my back. I shouted for Syl to switch it off for me. She started panicking, she was jumping up and down on the spot shouting, 'Stop messing about! Pack it in!'

I was in agony. I wasn't messing about. This thing had me in a wrestling hold, or so it felt. What a sight it must have been, my arm all twisted almost up my back and Syl jumping up and down panicking about how to turn it off.

That was an experience we will not forget in a long time. We carried on using the TENS but not on my elbow, just the shoulders and ankle. It was fine some of the time.

February came and Maureen, the physio-terrorist asked me to pose in the standing frame for some pictures for a display the physiotherapists were doing. Me pose in the standing frame? Oops! Now, I didn't like to be seen in it in the house, let alone pose in it for my picture to be taken. I was in a corner - how could I refuse after all that they had done for me. So, after a lot of talking I said that I would, but it didn't stop there. Oh, no.

They wanted some pictures of me getting on my stairlift, getting in my car, standing at the sink in the frame washing up. Washing up! Now that was a total con. I never washed up well when standing in the frame to do it. They were very grateful. I was very embarrassed. I felt such a tart when I saw the photos of me in the frame at the sink, pretending to wash up.

At the end of February I was having so much trouble with my legs that it stopped me from crawling altogether. I had done the odd few crawls when I could but now, as soon as I got on the floor, the pain would start. I went to the doctor's and they tried all the things that I had tried myself in the past to see if they worked. This time they didn't, so they increased the Carbamazepine tablets.

This seemed to do the trick but now I was taking six of these tablets a day, and the Baclofen, and the painkillers. It seemed that all I was doing was popping pills and that wasn't for me.

I had to go to see Doctor Walton at Tameside hospital. I told her that I thought I was going downhill fast. She asked me lots of questions about the things I was doing and the medication I was taking, then she gave me a thorough examination, after which we sat down and talked. She said I was in good health, really and quite fit but I needed to cut down on the exercises I was doing. She thought that the way I was pushing myself was one of the main contributors to the pain and I needed to cut back.

This was hard to accept but she was right. I was really pushing myself to the limit again but that was me. I needed to be fighting back, not sitting back, I wasn't the sort of person to just think about doing things, I always did them. I said that I would rest from doing too many exercises for a while if it would do me a bit of good. I stopped doing them for a few weeks just to give myself a break and it worked well. I picked up and the pains in my arms, for once, were easing a little.

I found that I was having to do a lot more transferring from chair to chair around the house now, anyway, and that alone was playing havoc with my arms. A typical day would be: I would be sitting in the armchair and I would need to go to the toilet. I would transfer from the armchair into my wheelchair, then go to the stairlift and transfer from the wheelchair onto that. The "Orient Express" would take me up the stairs to the landing where I would transfer onto the shower chair which I used to go to the toilet. I would then stand up, sort myself out, go to the loo, finish, then stand up again; pull everything up, wheel myself to the stairlift. Then I'd do everything again only in reverse order.

If I had a bad day and my bladder was playing up, which on many occasions it did, I would have to do this no end of times. But on a normal day I suppose I would only have to do this ten to fifteen times.

Then there were days that my bowels would be bad. This caused me some terrible embarrassment at times. I would just make it to the loo on some days, but others I would just get the urge to go, from out of the blue. I would go as quickly as I could to the stairlift, transfer to it and, nine times out of ten, I'd be on the "Orient Express" and it would be too late. I would mess myself. I punched and punched myself and called myself an animal for doing it.

Syl would tell me it was not my fault, it was my MS but this was no comfort. I was so ashamed. I messed myself a few times when the lads were about but they pretended not to notice and just got on with what they were doing. I so wish that my sons had never had to witness me doing this, for their sake and mine.

Syl told me to see the doctor about it but I was so ashamed and could not bring myself to talk about it. I watched everything I ate and would take laxatives to make myself more regular but still it would happen. The MS made it very difficult for me this way and it took me a long time to come to terms with this one and beat it, but I sorted it out and all is OK now (legs crossed!).

Well, over the weeks I had rested so much I felt back to my normal self, full of zip and wanting to do things. I got the Zimmer frame out at the top of the stairs, this was so I could do my hop-walk into the toilet to cut down on some of the transfers. What an excuse to cut down on transfers! I was doing it just to see if I could still do it and I could - just. But it was hard, very hard. I knew in my heart of hearts that I wasn't finished walking and my pride and determination will never, and I mean never, stop trying.

Chapter Sixteen

I got to May without too much of a problem, then I got in a pickle again by overdoing it. I fell while I was trying to use the Zimmer frame and this time broke my big toe. I was asked the question by someone, "Would I ever learn?".

The answer was, and still is, "No", because that wouldn't be me. This was my way, to do things till I couldn't physically do them any more. Now, once again I was going backwards.

Through this new injury, and all the sitting down that I had been doing, I had to get on the floor and do more of my pelvic work to get my lower-back and all that area stronger. I was doing well, I suppose, but then I started to tire really easily, and after doing only a few hundred sit-ups.

This wasn't me. I didn't fatigue that easily and not after only doing just those few bits of working-out. But I was and I couldn't for the life of me sleep at night for the pain in my legs. I tried the Night Nurse again to see if that would do anything for me. It was OK I suppose, I got a few hours sleep here and there but it was no answer to what I really needed - pain-free sleep.

I still woke up throughout the night with the pain, no matter what I did. And now, when the pain really took hold, my legs would go stiff, so stiff that there was no way that I could bend them when I lay down. Syl went out and bought one of those draught-excluders in the shape of a snake to put under my knees, for when I got in bed to see if that would break up the spasm. She had what I call her "Blue Peter head" on. She made it thicker and sturdier so that it would not give way under the pressure of my legs and it worked. My legs became a lot better at night-time and I was not waking up with spasms and stiffness in them.

I was given some foot drop splints to see if they would help with the pain in my legs, too. I had to wear them at night in bed and this, as you can imagine, was very uncomfortable and caused some problems, especially when I turned over. But it had to be done and it went some way in helping them. It certainly stopped me having the feeling of being pulled out of bed and I was getting some sleep now. Then, right on cue, and just when everything was on the mend again, the stairlift blew up.

Wonderful! Now I had the added problem of doing my Mission Impossible impression to get up and down the stairs. Mind you, the workmen were good and fixed it in a couple of days. While they were working on it I decided to give my car a clean. I washed the outside up to the parts that I could reach and then Syl finished off the rest for me.

While we were washing the car we somehow ended up having a silly row over something and nothing so it was chamois down and she stormed off into the house leaving me to get on with it. I thought, "sod it", and started to clean the inside of the car on my own. I did the front with no problem then I got into the back and started to clean that. I was having no problems, until I wanted to get back out and into my wheelchair. I was stuck! Stuck in the back of the car and no matter how hard I tried I couldn't for the life of me get out. I could see Syl looking though the window in the kitchen laughing her little head off at me.

There was no way I was going to shout for her to help me so I struggled, and struggled, till eventually, after three-quarters of an hour, I did it. I finally got out of the back of the car into my wheelchair and went into the kitchen where Syl was sitting drinking a cup of coffee.

'All done is it?' she said smirking and giggling. 'The back of that car must be really clean now, the amount of time you were in there.'

'Oh, aren't you smart?' I replied, feeling really pissed-off and gagging for a drink by this time. She stood looking at me with one of those fantastic smiles on her face. That did it we both just burst out laughing.

'I knew you were stuck. I could see you trying like mad to get out of the back,' she said.

Now this might come as a shock but I've never cleaned the back seats of the car since; I leave that job to Syl. I don't fancy the idea of getting stuck again.

The weather was fantastic and everyone was enjoying it, even me, but there were times when it was just too hot and I would just melt. Throughout this my MS played up and I would go very loose and just fall from side to side in my wheelchair. There was no way that I could wheel myself outside on those days, no matter how hard I tried so going round the shops or visiting friends had to be done early in the morning before dinner so it wasn't too hot.

Every July the Manchester branch of the Multiple Sclerosis Society went to Southport for a day out. We had been on the last couple of trips and they were great. We had our names down to go on this one. Usually we went in the Multiple Sclerosis Society branch ambulance but this time I thought that I would follow them in my car. The weather was fantastic, a real scorcher of a day with lovely clear blue skies and the sun beating down. One of those days on which, in the past, I used to love walking round with no shirt on and wearing shorts, you know them lazy chill-out, feel-good days. Wonderful stuff.

But this was now and there was no way that I could wear shorts. Not with my legs, now. God! The last time I saw legs like mine they were hanging out of a nest. Anyway, I had to wear a leg-bag on long trips like this, so that put paid to that. I had to wear my jeans and T-shirt and like it.

We got there just before dinner and had a quick sandwich while everyone gathered in the Floral Hall. The lads wanted to go off to the fun-fair with a couple of the other kids who were there from the Branch. I was a bit reluctant to let them go off on their own but in the end I gave in and gave them their money.

Off they all went to the fun-fair without a care in the world. That gave Syl and me the chance to look round the shops before we followed them. It was a lovely day. Like I say the place was packed with day-trippers, like us. Vest and me and a couple of others had a look round the shops.

We had a brew in one of the cafés then went to find the lads. It was easy enough to find them; well they found us. They had run out of money and needed some more. It's always the same - they don't want you tagging along with them one minute, then the money runs out and you're flavour of the month again.

We watched them go on some of the rides that were there and have a go at the side-shows, like darts and shooting. We all really enjoyed it. The day just flew past and soon it was time to go for tea in the Floral Hall. The branch always had a meal laid on there and it was always great. This year was no exception.

The meal was lovely and well organised, as usual, by Mary and the committee. It was so nice to go out and just enjoy yourself and not have to bother about anything for a change.

We left at about six and headed back to Manchester. I'm totally hopeless at getting home from Southport. I think the place is great but I hate the journey home because I always get lost, so I followed Mary and her daughter-in-law in their car. As soon as I saw the signs for the motorway I was OK. I just zoomed off into the sunset heading for home with the sound of one of the lads' rows brewing in the back of the car.

It always seemed to end the same way. We would have a good family day out and the lads would get on with each other all day until it was time to go home. This seemed to trigger it all off. They would decide that it was time to go back to winding each other up, calling each other stupid names, which in turn would run over into a bigger row that had Syl and me at it, too.

This used to send my MS up the wall and I would have to try hard to get it back into line and under control, plus it used to put me in some awfully sad moods. I could never see why they never wanted to get on with each other. I would take it to heart and blame myself for it all, thinking that if I were on my feet it would not happen. This was wrong. It didn't matter if I was on my feet or not, they had always been the same. They just loved to wind each other up, no matter how much trouble it caused - and it caused plenty over the years.

Syl and I tried everything we could to get them to get on but it seemed that they could only do this if it suited them. Don't get me wrong, they did get on and they loved each other but they just couldn't play together for any amount of time. They are two great lads who have their own likings and they would share each other's things some of the time. They would go out playing together but at the end of the day they just loved to have this little war going on to spoil it. Why?

170

Chapter Seventeen

On July the twenty-first my sister, Maureen, rang me to say that Mum had been taken into hospital and was very ill. I hadn't seen my mum in months - only from time to time on things like birthdays or Christmas. There had been a falling out in the family and this was the reason. It had been a few months since I last spoke to her on the telephone and then she was fine, or should I say that she made out she was.

I loved my mum and had missed her terribly over the last few years. There wasn't a day went by that I didn't speak of her to the lads. Not having her coming round to our house, as she had done for so many years to talk to and ask her advice on things, and to have her share her life with the two lads, cut me up inside.

I used to see her on the market. She would look at me and I'd look at her, neither of us speaking to the other, just a little gesture, that's all. This hurt me and I know it hurt her. I would go back to the car and bury my head in my hands. The pain I felt inside is something nobody should ever have to go through.

I went to the hospital to see her and when I got there our Moie (Maureen) was there at Mum's bedside with my nephew, Nick. Mum was just lying there in bed. She was very ill. She was no stranger to hospitals and over the years I had seen her in some very poorly ways but never anything as bad as the way she was that day. I held Mum's hand for a few minutes until a doctor called our Moie and me outside for a chat. Our Nick came with us.

The doctor told us that Mum had stomach cancer. That minute my world fell in. Our Moie just burst out crying uncontrollably and she was visibly shaking. Our Nick looked at me, fighting back the tears, then just hurriedly walked towards the door shaking his head in disbelief.

Our Moie was holding herself up, somehow, by the wall with the help of a Sister who was there. I think that was the only time I've ever wanted my wheelchair.

I could feel my legs caving in under me. It was like I had just taken twenty Baclofen loosening tablets all at once. I was like a jelly.

The lump I had in my throat was so tight it was choking me. I was spluttering and sobbing at the same time. I couldn't see through the tears in my eyes.

'My mum! Not my mum! You've got it wrong. Please!' I pleaded.

I looked over to our Moie. She was totally gone. The Sister was trying to comfort her. I couldn't get near to her to hold her. I just wanted to put my arms around her and hold her tight. I wanted to be there for her. Our Nick came back up the corridor a few minutes later, crying. We all just looked at each other not knowing what to say, so nobody said anything.

The Sister asked us if we would like her to come back in with us to tell Mum but we thought it best to leave it till she was feeling stronger.

We sorted ourselves out, then after a few more minutes we went back in to see Mum. She was no fool. She gave us all a look, a look that I have seen on her face a thousand times before. We sat there that day in hospital, all of us with the same expression on our faces, an expression of total disbelief.

Within the next few days Mum had picked up well. She looked ten times better than she had done, so we decided that it was the right time to tell her, if there is a right time to tell someone this.

We asked the Sister to come in with us and help us to tell Mum. She said that she thought it best if she told her, it would be better that way. God, my heart was racing and beating like never before. We went in to Mum. Moie, Nick and I stood round the bed and the Sister pulled the curtain. Our Moie took hold of Mum's hand and gave it a squeeze, a tear slowly rolling down her face.

Nick took hold of her other hand. I couldn't get my wheelchair down the side of the bed so I got as near as I could and just reached out for her.

The Sister began telling Mum; her face went ashen and then lost all colour. Our Moie threw her arms around Mum, our Nick reached out to me. I could not hear or see my mum, I was so far gone with emotion.

Mum took it very well. She looked at us and never said a word. I think she already knew, I honestly do think that. Our Moie was breaking her heart on Mum's shoulder. I wanted to do the same. I wanted to hug her like there was no tomorrow but I couldn't reach her, so I just sat there in my wheelchair at the end of the bed, crying.

I felt the Sister put her arm on my shoulder and give it a squeeze. Then she left. I followed her, went out into the main corridor and just looked out of the window, crying and thinking about all the things that Mum had done for us.

Mum had brought us up on her own and had done a fantastic job of it. We wanted for nothing. She had always been there for us through thick and thin but now she was going to leave us.

Over the next few days Mum seemed to really pick up well. She had this wonderful spirit about her, so full of zest and vigour and she had a wonderful colour in her face. She was more like her old self.

Our Tim had come down from Wales so the whole family was now there. We sat around Mum's bed and we all had some good laughs about certain things that had happened throughout our lives.

Syl was dropping me off at the hospital in the morning then sorting out, throughout the day, what had to be done, then she would rush back to the hospital with the lads for an hour or so. She was a star.

My legs, by now, were starting to play up and were very sore through lack of exercising. I hadn't had any chance to do any as I was up early in the morning, a quick shower then straight out to the hospital to spend the day with Mum. At night when we got in it was a quick tea and play with the lads, then on the floor for some stretching. This didn't do that much good but it was all I could manage to do, so I took plenty of painkillers and loosening tablets and just took the pain.

Our Moie had to work until dinnertime so she could only make it after two o'clock but then she would spend the rest of the day there with Mum. Our Nick would come with her or he would even come with me. He seemed to spend every hour he could with his nan;

so did Tim, he felt the same, we all did.

After ten days Mum was allowed home, she was going to stay with our Moie and Nick at Moie's maisonnette over the shops. I picked Mum up in my car with our Moie and Nick and dropped them off at the maisonnette. I said I would let Mum get settled for a day then come and see her.

The next day Mum came to our house to see me with our Nick. Syl went and picked her up. Mum wasn't too well but she wanted to come. She was always the same. She would push it to the limit. We had a good old natter about this and that and she told me how she had missed visiting us. That's just how I felt. I looked at my mum as she sat on the settee. This once tall and beautiful woman was now so frail and wracked in pain. I felt so guilty that she had made this effort to come and see us and I was just so glad to see her in my house once again.

She could only stay for a few minutes but that, to me, was everything. Syl and Nick helped Mum back into the car and took her back to our Moie's flat. That was the very last time my mum came to our house, or went out again.

After that I went to see her at our Moie's. I had to have our Nick to lift me into the wheelchair with help from Syl to get me up the flight of stairs. If our Tim was there he would lift me out of the chair and carry me, while someone brought the wheelchair up. This was hard work for everyone but nobody was bothered, except me. It hurt me so much inside, having to be lifted and carried. I wanted to try to get myself up the stairs but they were hard, cold stone and too difficult. This was something that I couldn't accept, but I had to for Mum's sake.

She was now getting worse and had to be in bed all the time as it was too difficult for her to get about. Moie and Nick were nursing her and doing a fantastic job. They did everything for her. Mum was in really good spirits, laughing and joking with us. Our Moie and Nick looked very tired, as they were on the go all the time.

My MS was taking a massive battering with all the stress and worry and I was in so much pain with my legs. I had to wear drop splints all day and all night to see if that would help ease the leg pain. It didn't. I had even lost the feeling in my left leg and couldn't wriggle my toes.

I was going to see Mum all day then trying to come home

and exercise but I could not concentrate. I just wanted to be with my mum no matter how much pain I was in. I wasn't sleeping, nor was Syl. She was so worried about the state I was getting in that she was getting herself in a worse state than me.

It was so hard to get into our Moie's flat, very hard. First it was the two flights of stairs outside, leading to the flat, then there was another set of stairs inside, leading to the bedroom where Mum was. When I got in Nick would carry my wheelchair to the top of the stairs and I would go up the stairs on my bum, one at a time, with Syl moving my legs for me as I went up.

I then spent the day in the bedroom talking to my mum, with our Moie and Nick and whoever else turned up to see her, and there were lots of people. Mum was starting to go downhill and she was on a lot of medication to help her with her pains and discomfort.

On Tuesday the ninth of August, our Nick and Gary got me up the outside stairs and into the flat, where from then on I did my "stair by stair on my bum" bit to get to the top of the landing and into my wheelchair. They would have carried me but the stairs weren't wide enough and I wouldn't let them anyway. I had to do my bit.

Our Nick watched over me like a hawk on every stair I went up. I could see him out of the corner of my eye, itching to help me. He is so loving and concerned. He calls me "our kid" and always has done since we were kids. Our Moie did all she could to make life easier for me to get around when I finally got to the top of the stairs and into my wheelchair; nothing was too much trouble for her.

I got into the bedroom to find Mum very ill. She was so much worse than she had been the day before. I got as close to her as I could and held her hand. She gave me one of her looks, a look that tells you everything without saying a word. I felt so good just being there and holding her hand; being able to do this and feel her love was all I could ask for.

We started to talk about the kids and how they had grown up so quickly and what a good wife Syl was. Mum said how well she looked after the lads and me, and always would do.

We got talking about old times, like when I was a lad and what a little sod I had been and all the silly things I used to do. Then she said that I had always been a good son and never brought trouble to the door.

I looked into her eyes as I held her hand so tight, smiled and said, 'Remember the bomb, Mum?'

She laughed and told me to tell her the story again. We had told this story so many times to each other over the years.

Well, the story behind it was when I was a kid about eight the rag-and-bone man came into our street with his cart. He used to give you a bow and arrow or a balloon if you gave him some unwanted clothes, brass or metal - anything of use. Well I wanted a bow and arrow, so this day I went up to his cart to see what I could see and I saw this dirty black tube-like thing and asked him what it was. He told me it was a bomb from the First World War. That was it! I had to have this bomb. We were going to play war next and all the lads in the street already had their guns ready to play, so this was the ideal thing for me to have: a real bomb!

I ran into the house to find Mum but she wasn't there. I had a look round the house to see what we didn't need but there wasn't anything I could find. So I looked a bit harder and I found this old coat hanging behind the door and ran back to the cart with it.

Now Mum was always going on about this coat, saying that it was no good, so I offered him that. The man swapped the coat for the bomb, and I went back into the house to get a gun so I could play war with the other kids in the street. Just as I was going out, Mum came back and asked me what the dirty thing was I was carrying. I told her it was my bomb and started to go out the door.

'Where did you get a bomb from?' she asked, looking puzzled.

'I swapped that old coat for it,' I told her, then tried again to go out to play.

'What coat?' she asked me, speaking through her teeth.

Now Mum had this way of speaking to me like a ventriloquist. She would have a smile on her face and talk through her teeth and her lips never moved. She was really good at it, especially when people were about. Now when she spoke like this to me there was always a great sense of pain to follow, and it was always in my direction. Her face said it all. I was in trouble, big trouble.

I stood looking at her with this bomb in my hand, hoping that it would go off and quick.

'What coat? I asked you!'

I gulped and somehow stuttered out, 'That old coat of yours.'

'Ahhh My coat! My coat! I'll kill you, you little ******!'

That was it. Time to run, and I mean run. I tried to get through the door and round to our Moie's house and safety.

'My coat! My coat! You little......!' She had me by my shirt and pulled me towards her, still screaming at me.

'Tell me who you swapped it with!' she yelled.

'No, you'll hit me,' I screamed, as I tried even harder to escape her clutches.

'I won't!' she yelled, red-faced. 'Just tell me who's got my coat.'

Just then the cavalry arrived in the shape of our Moie.

'Stop her! She's going to kill me,' I said to her as I got free from Mum's hold.

'What's going on?' asked Moie, looking totally bemused. I held on to the back of our Moie as I positioned her between Mum and me.

Mum told her what had gone on then they both turned to me, giving me this look. Then our Moie asked me in a nice quiet, calm way what I had done with the coat. I looked at her and very sheep-ishly said, 'I swapped it for this bomb with the rag and bone man.'

'Ahhh! The rag and bone man! The rag and bone man!' Mum said, dancing on the spot in this really weird way.

'Calm down, Mum! Just calm down while he tells us.'

Our Moie knelt down, looked me in the face and asked me, all calm-like, 'When did you swap it with him, Gary?'

'Not long ago, well just a bit really,' I said, looking over her shoulder at Mum.

'He'll be miles away with it by now,' Mum said, still yelling.

'Calm down, Mother!' Moie said to her. 'We'll get it back, don't worry.'

I was praying that she was right, because the look Mum had on her face said that I was about to get the tanning of my life if she didn't get it back.

'Right. I will go and see if I can find him in one of the streets. Mum, you stay here with our Gary till I get back,' our Moie said to Mum as she was walking out of the door.

'No! Moie, I'll come with you,' I said grabbing her hand as I glared bog-eyed at Mum inching towards me. 'She'll kill me if you go.'

'Now don't be stupid. Mum's not going to do anything, are

you, Mum?' Moie said, looking long and hard at the both of us.

The look on Mum's face was one we both knew, so she told Mum to come with her to look for the rag and bone man and told me to stay in the house and not to move until they got back in.

So off they went with my bomb to get the coat back. In the meantime I just looked through the window of the house, panicking and hoping everything went well. They seemed to be gone ages, then they appeared at the top of the street. I couldn't see them carrying the coat, so that was it. As soon as the door opened I made a run for the back door, ran into the outside toilet and locked myself in.

I was scared stiff. I don't know why, as Mum never really hit me - I just made out that she did. I sat there on that toilet looking under the door to see if anyone was coming to get me and within minutes they did. It was our Moie knocking on the toilet door telling me not to worry as all was going to be OK and to come back into the house. I gently pulled back the bolt on the toilet door and slowly opened it, just enough to see her face. She smiled at me, called me a silly sod, and told me to come out. I did and we both went into the house but with me still hiding behind her. I could see Mum sitting on the sofa having a drink and she was looking right at me; but this time she had her calm head on.

'Sorry, Mum,' I said as I went and sat next to her. She ruffled my hair, read me the riot act then gave me a big squeeze and laughed.

It all ended up that our Moie had to buy the bomb to get Mum's coat back. It cost her a couple of shillings and me a very sore bum.

I was telling Mum this story as she lay there in bed and everything was going great when, for no reason, I just started to cry. I tried so very hard to hold it in but there was no way I could. She wiped the tears from my face and told me not to cry. I put my arms around her and just held her as close as I could. I stayed there like that for a few minutes, just holding her then I told her how much I loved her. She stroked my hair and smiled one of her smiles, the sort that said it all. We carried on chatting for a while longer but then she tired, so I just sat there holding her hand and looking at her face, remembering all those wonderful days we had together.

My legs started to play up. They were giving me the most terrible pain and I was in agony with them, but I didn't care. All I wanted was to be there for my mum. Our Moie came in and told me to go home and get some rest and try to sort myself out with some exercises to ease the pain. So I went home and did some standing in my standing frame for an hour or so then did some working-out. It seemed that I was never going to stop. I just kept on exercising and exercising, trying to rid myself of this hurting I had inside of me. In the end I just lay there on the floor, totally exhausted and drained.

Syl walked in and told me to have a shower and relax for a while, then go to bed. We sat there in bed all that night just talking about what had happened in the daytime and what my mum and I had talked about.

I was up bright and early on the Wednesday morning. I was in lots of pain and my MS thought that it was time it made an appearance. My hands and arms were trembling and going into spasm. I took loads of pills to help see me through the day, all the things that I would need to help me be there for Mum.

Syl drove me to our Moie's. Our Nick came down to help Syl get me up the stairs. He told us Mum had had a bad night and wasn't very good. When I went into the bedroom she had been propped up by our Moie, who had made her nice and comfy. Mum was just staring straight out in front of her at the wall.

The strain had caught up with our Moie. She had passed out through not sleeping and our Nick was just as bad. He had only slept a few hours himself. I stayed with Mum while Nick got his head down for a few hours and our Moie had a lie down on top of her bed. I sat there at the side of the bed, holding Mum's hand. She was fighting for every breath she took, her eyes motionlessly staring at the wall.

As I was holding Mum's hand my body was twisting and turning, I was in so much pain. I took Tylex painkillers to try to ease it, but they were doing no good. I stayed there at Mum's side until gone six o'clock and she had not moved. I watched her every minute and at times it seemed that she had stopped breathing. There wasn't a sound coming from her.

Where one second earlier there had been this terrible dull ache of her fighting for life, there was now this so eerie silence. Then her breath would shudder and she'd fight on. My eyes now were so red with crying that I could no longer see the few feet away to where Mum was laying. I so wanted this awful thing to end, yet I couldn't bear the thought of losing Mum.

Our Moie told me to go home and get some rest, but I didn't want to. I wanted to stay with Mum but this MS wouldn't let me. It kept on and on at me till in the end I was so uncomfortable, and in so much pain, that I had to go home. Before I went I told our Moie to ring me if anything happened. All night I was tossing and turning just grabbing five minutes' sleep here and there, wondering how Mum was and if everything was OK.

Then at five fifty the phone rang. Syl answered it. It was our Moie to tell me Mum had died at five forty-two. I put my head under the pillow. I didn't want to hear it. No! No! Not Mum please! Not my Mum.

I loved her so very, very much. Syl put her arms around me and pulled me close to her and just held me there as tight as she could. All I could think of then was our Moie. She and Mum went everywhere together, they were never apart - they were inseparable.

Syl helped me to get dressed and drove me round to our Moie's. It was early in the morning and there was nobody about to help us get up the stairs. I told her to go and get our Nick. She told me to shush and, I will never know how, picked me up in the wheelchair and carried me up the two flights of stairs. Words can't describe how I felt at her doing this.

We knocked on our Moie's door. She opened it with a startled look on her face. When I told her what Syl had just done she couldn't believe it. I asked Syl if she was OK. She said she was fine. Our Moie looked as though she had shed an ocean of tears, her eyes all red and puffy.

I got to the bottom of the stairs and started to crawl up. Our Nick wanted to help me, so did Syl, but this was something I had to do. I wanted to do it myself and see my mum. I got to the top and tried to crawl to the bedroom door but my legs were so stiff they would not bend, so I dragged myself there, lying flat on the floor, by my elbows.

As I reached the bedroom door I could see my mum still propped up so nice and comfy, as she had been the day before when I left her. Her eyes were still open, staring at the same spot on the wall. I wanted to get to her to close them but this bastard MS wouldn't let me. For once it had beaten me!

I just sat there on the floor at the bottom of the bed, reaching out crying and wishing that I could just reach her and hold her in my arms to hold her so very close to me and say my final goodbye.

Our Nick came and helped me back downstairs. We all sat there in the living room, numb, saying very little. Our Tim arrived and went upstairs to Mum. You could hear him crying for his nanna. He came down, his eyes as red as everyones in the room. He gave us all a hug that started us all crying again.

The undertakers came, shortly after the doctor had been, to take Mum away. Our Tim told them to take great care of his nanna.

A few days later Syl and I went to the Chapel of Rest to see my mum for the last time. I kissed her and told her that I loved her and thanked her for being my mum.

Mum was cremated on the sixteenth of August, the day before my birthday. Nick, Tim and some close friends carried Mum's coffin as I sat there in my wheelchair wishing that I could have at least done this one thing in life for the woman who had carried me all of mine. Thanks to the MS I couldn't.

GOOD NIGHT, MAM. (PEG.)

Chapter Eighteen

To say my MS had taken a battering over the last few weeks would be an understatement, to say the least. I was totally down and almost out. I hadn't been so low physically for a long time. I was drained: my get up and go had got up and gone. I needed a shot in the arm to help me (or in my case, in the bum). I needed a course of steroids to help me get back to some semblance of normality. So I went to the doctor's and I was put on a course of steroid injections to help me, and as usual they started to work pretty quickly. That was just what I needed - the steroids getting round my body fast so I could get myself moving again.

Within a couple of weeks I was back on the floor doing my usual things and getting my legs into some sort of routine again. I was doing lots of weights and press-ups to get my arms in shape. I was doing plenty of sit-ups and back exercises to help my posture The one thing I did plenty of was crawling, something I could still do to get around the house under my own steam. Everything was going well on that front; I was beginning to feel as though I was my old self again.

In September the Multiple Sclerosis Society branch had a cheese and wine night. It was a good night, well it was for Vest. She "tested" that many bottles of different wine she was "kettled" - drunk. This was the first time in a very long time that she had let her hair down in this way. She was normally a laugh a minute without wine. Now, well she never stopped all the way home in the car, laughing and singing. She was full of it, the wine that is. It was good to see her let her hair down for once. If anyone deserved a good night out then she did and she'd had one.

We had just gone through some very hard weeks with my

mum, and Syl had been my backbone. She was the one that had held me together, she was the one that was helping me emotionally, now, through these days of me one minute being OK and the next breaking down in tears because I had remembered something that Mum had said or done.

All these different emotions were making my fight with MS so very hard. I could cope with the everyday battle to keep fit but this, this was something that I couldn't overcome on my own. Syl was my rock.

We were coming around to "normal" again. Well, in a sort of fashion but it did seem that every time we got on an even keel and everything was going well something happened. Yet again, it did. The stairlift broke down again. So there I was, back doing my Mission Impossible impression again, up and down the stairs every time I wanted to use the toilet.

I was doing lots of standing in the standing frame and my legs were feeling the benefit from it, in fact with the steroids and the standing my legs were looking quite good. They were getting to be muscular which made a nice change from the sparrow legs of old. I was doing lots of wheelchair exercises, too, so I could build up my stamina. I was doing well but I wasn't doing as well as I normally did, because it didn't matter what I did within a few days I was back to good old square one.

By now I had finished the course of steroids and it was down to just little old me to do it without their help. I didn't last long. Oh! I tried and I tried but it didn't matter, the MS was back and it seemed to be getting stronger, so I went to see Doctor Sambrook. We had a good chat and discussed the ins and outs of the things wrong with me. He thought that the only option left open to me now was to have steroids each week for as long as it took.

I had nothing but total respect for this man. He put a good case to us and he was right, the only things that worked was the A.C.T.H. steroids, so I said, Yes.

With that he wrote to my doctor's to tell them what was going to happen with my new treatment and to start me on the injections. I was to start on a high dose to see how it went, then have it adjusted accordingly. Well with all the pain I was having and the weakness and loss of feeling in certain parts of my body it seemed to be the only hope I had left. So, it was now down to the injections each week and me.

Within a couple of weeks I had started the treatment. I was going to the doctor's once a week so the District Nurse could administer the injection. It was a high dose of Adrenocorticotropic hormone (A.C.T.H.) to start off with: eighty millilitres (two units), once a week. Usually, when I was on a course of steroids, I would have eighty millilitres for the first two days, then cut down to forty millilitres for the next four days, then twenty millilitres for the last four days. Now on this new treatment I was having the eighty millilitres once a week. I was told to cut it down if and when I thought that I could manage on a lower dose.

With the course that I had not long finished, and this one now starting, I was getting to look like the Michelin Man around the face again. In fact, I had more chins than a Chinese phone book, but I could cope with that because I was feeling the benefits of the injections within the first couple of weeks. I could look forward to having a good Christmas now and enjoy it rather than face the one I had been expecting only a few weeks earlier.

Everything was great. We were ready to do all the shopping and get the presents for everyone, and we had the Multiple Sclerosis Society party coming up which was always good - it was my chance to have a few drinks. I was doing well with my crawling and I had a couple of goes at walking with the Zimmer frame and that wasn't too bad either. So all in all everything was rosy. The only problem I had was that the pain in my leg wasn't going any easier and it was causing me to have a lot of sleepless nights. I was back to sitting on the side of the bed, when it woke me in the night, and trying to massage the pain away, which never worked.

I tried all the old things I had tried in the past, like taking Night Nurse flu remedy to help me sleep, but that didn't work this time, nor did the herbal sleeping pills Syl got me.

So I went to see the doctor and I was given a short course of mild sleeping pills to help me sleep and told to up the dose of Carbamazepine to see if that would help ease the ankle and leg pain.

We went to the Multiple Sclerosis Society party and it was great. I took our Moie, as I thought that it would be nice if we went out together for once. As usual the party was a good one and a good night was had by all. It was nice to see old mates and to have a good natter about this and that. Some of my friends were not too good, in fact one of them, Paul, was having a very bad time of it because of his MS. It was giving him hell. I found myself thanking God that I was on this treatment and able to fight on. How long for, well, I didn't know, as there are no certainties with this disease.

These were the only times that I spoke about my MS - with other MS sufferers or medical people.

I always found that if some able-bodied person comes up to you and asks, "How are you?" and you prattle on about things like, "Oh, my MS is at it", "I'm not feeling too good", "My sore leg", or, "I'm on new pills", they soon lose interest quickly.

Not many people want to go into all the details. So when people asked me how I was I said, "Great no problems.".

Then there are the days when you get people who ask you what's wrong with you. I was once sat outside a shop in my wheelchair, my mind miles away waiting for Syl, and this face came from nowhere, grinning from ear to ear looking me right in the eyes, scaring me half to death and asks me the question, 'What's wrong with you then?'

I did an acrobatic sort of twist in my chair, as I was muttering about having MS. Well after that I got fed up of saying, "I've got MS." so I made things up like, "I've got Alice disease?".

When they asked what it was I said, "I don't know but Christopher Robin went down with it.".

They'd look at me as if I was simple and, you know what? On those sorts of days I am, I just don't care.

Another year was coming to a close and it had been the hardest yet for me. This was the first Christmas without my mum and I really felt it. I wished in my heart of hearts that she could have been there with us as it would have been the first Christmas that we had had together in a long time. But it wasn't to be. We had a wonderful time and the New Year was a really good one. I got absolutely "kettled" with our Nick and Tim.

I was so drunk that I could not get on the stairlift to go upstairs without help. But for once when I did get into bed I slept and slept. The last year had been an eye-opener for me. I just hoped that the year ahead would be kinder to us.

Well 1995 started with me feeling good but I looked as though I was on an eat-everything-you-see diet. I was fat, and I mean fat. I was so fat-looking that my face was round and bloated. It wasn't through the food I was eating, but the steroids and the water I was retaining. So I had one of my brainwaves: "Cut the amount of fluids that I drank.".

I was doing it again. I had been here before doing the same sort of thing and I was wrong then. But I thought, "Well! That was then and this is now.". So I started to cut down on drinking and to no one's surprise, even mine, I got a kidney infection.

I passed out through the pain of it all, I was so ill, but I just never learned. I looked in the mirror and staring back at me was this fat-faced person - me. I could never think of the things that were good, just the downside of the treatment and this was the problem. Never mind that the big toe on my right foot had moved for the first time in ages. Or that I was able to do my hop-walk from the stairs to the kitchen, every now and then, on the Zimmer frame. I was even doing my wheelchair transfers a lot better because I was stronger in myself, but this didn't matter because all I could think of was the downside of it - the weight.

I would, at times, take it to heart when someone would say to me, "You've put weight on, Gary.".

It made me feel really down inside, as though I was overeating and I wasn't, it was all down to the steroids. The fact was that I normally looked so drawn in the face that a bit of a change made a big difference to my appearance. The people who'd said it meant no harm. It was me, again, looking for reasons to stop having the injections and lose the appearance I hated, stopping the treatments would have been worse.

So I carried on with them, which in turn enabled me to carry on doing the things that I once normally did in my life.

There were other symptoms caused by the steroids, besides the water retention. There was this terrible feeling of having a burning in my right leg when I had just had the injection; my blood pressure - now this one was really annoying. One minute I was OK, the next I looked like Rudolf, the Red-Nosed Reindeer. Syl could have turned the lights out some nights and read a book, the glow from me was that bright!

Other problems were, if I was eating a toffee, or having a pudding or just a cup of coffee when I was out, the redness would suddenly appear. All these things made it very difficult to carry on with the treatment but I did. I persevered and tackled all the problems one by one as they arose.

Then there were the good things on the day after the injection; it was as if I was continent again. I was able to go all day without the need to suddenly rush off to the toilet. This would only last a couple of days but it was great while it lasted.

The pains I once had in my shoulders had now gone and the amount of work that I could do again was great, so all these pluses evened it up a touch. But not even the steroids could get rid of the pains in my legs or help me to sleep at night. In fact the opposite was now true. I was more awake than normal.

I had so much energy at times that when I was going to bed I would have to do something like two hundred sit-ups and some press-ups just to tire me out. Many times in the night I would get on the bedroom floor and do some working-out on my legs to either ease the terrible burning pain or to just loosen them off.

Then Maureen the physio-terrorist asked me if I would like to try some acupuncture on my right ankle to see if that would help. Well there was nothing to lose so I said, 'Why not?'

The acupuncture was fine but I looked like a pincushion at the end of it all when Maureen had finally stuck all the needles in me. The very first night after having the acupuncture my ankle wasn't too bad; I could get to sleep for once.

I got up the next morning, full of go and the first thing I did I was to get on the Zimmer frame at the bottom of the stairlift and give the ankle a try-out. I was going round the house like a demon, well, to the kitchen and back to the stairlift, but that was good, the feeling that I had inside was fantastic. I had the bug again now for walking, even though I was hurting my arms and my ankle wasn't great - No, that didn't matter. I had to be back on my feet, I was "Mister Determined" again. I decided to split the steroid injection up into two lower doses instead of having just the one needle of eighty millilitres once a week. I began having forty millilitres, twice a week. This was great for my toilet trouble. I was now able to have four instead of two days that I didn't have to rush to the loo all the time to pass water. This idea was a lot better; it seemed to be working well, so I was now going to the doctor's twice a week, on Mondays and Thursdays, for the nurse to administer the injections.

There was talk in the papers of a new wonder-drug that helped MS sufferers. It was called Beta Interferon. I made some enquiries about it and was told the price. The injections would cost in the region of ten thousand pounds a year. Ten grand! Talk about over-pricing things. This was supposed to be the wonder-drug to help MS sufferers. At those prices there was no way that the normal everyday bloke on the street could afford it. You would have to be loaded, and I mean loaded, to be able to have this treatment.

Well, there was no chance of me getting that treatment. Our National Health Service would be hard pushed to give it to everyone, and those lucky few who were getting it now were paying for it them-selves, so another new wonder-drug was out of reach for me.

Maureen, the physio-terrorist, and Mary Bown had been having conversations about this new wheelchair that was on the mar-ket. It raised you to a standing position and, without me knowing, they and the Multiple Sclerosis Society branch had organised for me to have one. I had seen them in the Multiple Sclerosis Society maga-zine and they looked wonderful. When they told me I was going to have one I was over the moon. This would mean that the old stand-ing frame, which I had used for so long, could now be sorted out and re-used.

I was so excited about getting this chair; just the fact that I could stand up when and where I liked was great. Not having to stay in the one spot all the time like I had to in the old standing frame was marvellous. I would now be free to do as I wanted.

The man came out to give me a demonstration model and show me how it all worked. It was great, it was so easy to use it was like a normal wheelchair to get around in then, when I wanted to stand up, I put the strap across my knees and pressed the switch up.

It was so much easier to get in than the old standing frame I had been using for so long. When I used that I had to pull myself up at the sink out of my wheelchair, then Syl would guide my legs into the frame and then strap me in. The first time I used the new chair I got this weird feeling going up. One minute I was sitting down, the next I was up in a standing position and I hadn't had to use my arms to pull myself up as normal. It was no struggle. I couldn't wait till I got my own to use.

We were in need of a holiday so we booked one in a disabled caravan at the Haven Holiday Centre in Wales. Syl's sister, Joyce, and brother, Richard, along with their families were also going to be there.

It seemed a good place to go. The caravan we had was brilliant. It had a ramp up to the door and inside there was plenty of room for my wheelchair. I could get into the bedroom and the toilet without any problems, and the beauty of it all was that I didn't have to crawl. I used the wheelchair all the time. The access around the camp wasn't too bad - it was quite flat. It was going to make for a good week's holiday, or so we thought.

Even the lads were having a good time. They were for the first few days, always around the places we thought that they would be - the pool, the fun-fair and beach. Then! It seemed that within a couple of days they had sprouted horns. We didn't know them, they were two different people. They were growing up fast and now they were making their own fun.

They were drinking and smoking behind our backs. Their attitudes had totally changed. They didn't want to listen to anything we had to say. All they wanted to do was get drunk and fall about like a pair of fools. They had got in with another bunch of lads, a bit older than they were, and all these lads were doing was standing about causing a nuisance, bullying the other kids who were trying to have a good time. And now our two were trying to do the same. This wasn't them, they were normally two good lads but within this short space of time they had grown into something that Syl and I didn't like. We just didn't know them anymore.

The arguments were going on all through the holiday. We were constantly having to check the lads for the things they were doing. This was to be the start of something that would get worse as the years went on. We had gone away for a family holiday but it ended up a total shambles thanks to the lads' stupid selfishness.

It wasn't too long after we got home from holiday that the standing wheelchair was delivered. I was never out of it. I was standing something like five hours day and after about a week or so my legs started to ache. I was told that I was overdoing it and to cut down on the amount of times I was standing. It would be best if I only stood for short periods, instead of an hour at a time like I had been doing.

We got to July and everything was great. Vest and I went shopping to one of the local supermarkets. She was getting some fruit and I was looking at the flowers next to the entrance. There were two women, the really stuck-up type. You know the sort I mean, "fur coat, no knickers"; "ten-bob millionaires" -that sort. Well I was looking at the flowers and I was just about to get some for Vest when one of them gave me a really dirty look and pushed in front of me.

So I said, 'Sorry love, am I in your way?' And I moved over to the other side so she could get in.

With that, the other one turned to me and said, 'Now you are in my way.'

She then whispered in a low voice to her mate, 'People like that shouldn't be allowed out.'

I was totally gutted at what the snotty cow said but I was so taken aback that I sat there like a total wally and watched them walk away without saying a word to them. I was, for once, lost for words. I have, many times, been sat outside shops when people have come up to me and asked me if I needed anything from the shop.

Once a lady with a few kids, her hands full with shopping, asked me if I needed anything from the shop I was sitting outside. That's how nice people really are, not like this pair of "ten-bobs" out doing their daily (moaning) shopping.

Chapter Nineteen

We got some great news. Our Tim's wife, Gaynor, had just had a baby boy called Toby; he was the first on my side of the family. We were all over the moon. Our Tim was so proud, he was telling me over the phone how wonderful the baby was so I took us all down to Chester to see the happy family. It was so nice to see my little nephew, Tim with a son of his own.

We went to Southport for a day out with the Multiple Sclerosis Society again and the lads, like the last time, did their own thing. It was a good job really because I was in terrible pain all day with my legs. It didn't matter what I did, or took, I could not shift the pain.

There was a masseuse who was taking his exams and wanted an MS patient to work with to see if massage would help. It didn't, it just toned up the muscles in my leg but the pain never moved.

August was with us and once again I got a bad water infection but this one laid me up for the best part of three weeks. I spent most of the time in bed I was that ill through it all. I had never had so much time on my hands, time to think and look at my life and I didn't like what I was looking at.

The most obvious was that I was hurting myself with things that I did, things like pushing myself too hard trying to walk on the Zimmer frame. My pride, and the urge that I had to walk again, wouldn't allow me just to sit about and watch the world pass me by. That was why I was overworking myself and pushing things to the limit, and beyond.

When I was laid up in bed with all that time on my hands I couldn't work out what was best for me. I was, for once, lost as to what would be the best thing to do. I could either carry on as I had been by crawling and using the Zimmer frame and take the pain, which might lead to something worse in the future; or I could stop doing all the exercises and just get about in the wheelchair, which really I was doing anyway, and had been for so long now.

Even though I wasn't really walking and it was my arms that were taking all the weight of my body, I was still on my feet and to me that was everything. I couldn't stop, no matter what pain I caused myself. I needed this because it was, as I saw it, my only chance of being whole again.

But I knew I needed help, so I asked for it. I went to see Doctor Walton and she referred me for a course of physiotherapy at the hospital. I though, great, I'll soon be on my feet again once I'm using their equipment.

Wrong! When I went to the hospital for my appointment I got the knock-back. They told me they were too busy to put me on the list and that they would ask for the Community Physiotherapist to call and give me physiotherapy at my home.

Talk about me being smacked in the teeth. There I was, ready and willing, and all I needed was them to give me back my "able" by letting me use their equipment and I got nothing. Zilch! No disrespect to the Community Physiotherapists - they do a great job, but they are limited in their resources I needed; things they had at the hospital like the pool, the parallel bars, the things that took the weight off my arms and put it back on my feet. I had been referred to the hospital by my specialist, Doctor Walton, for treatment but it didn't seem to matter - what she had told them I needed. They had passed the buck over to someone else, and that hurt me deeply.

So now I was back to that square one again. I had so much energy pent up inside me, and an urge to get going but I wasn't able to use it to my advantage. Their refusal made up my mind for me, I would carry on as I had been. I would use the Zimmer frame to hop-walk and sod them all: I would do it my way!

I thought, "Who knows? With the help of the physio-terrorist, and the wheelchair which stood me up, my legs might become strong enough to hold me up on their own.".

Who was I kidding? Nobody, but myself, I was getting worse with every day and that was a fact. The MS was getting the better of me and I had been denied the one thing that helped me fight back.

I was now really struggling, when I stood to use the Zimmer frame, or pull up my pants in the toilet, my back just gave way. I stooped so far forwards I looked like one of those ventriloquist's dolls when they take a bow.

The muscles in my bottom and about half-way up my back were now so very weak I was trying everything that I knew to strengthen them, but nothing was working. I was doing all the things that I was told to do, and more, but the one thing that I couldn't do was the exercise on my lower-back. The one where I lay on my back with my knees up and tried to lift my bottom off the floor. I tried and tried but it did no good.

So, I got on the floor and knelt up holding on to my wheel-chair, then lowered myself as slowly as I could and tried to get up this way. This was hard and I lost count of the amount of times that I couldn't get back up or just slumped to the floor in a heap.

But I was doing it and some days it made a difference. Some days it didn't but I had to carry on. This was it, this was all I could do on my lower-back to fight back, I didn't know what else to do.

I was doing fine with everything else. I was having no problems, but this, this was the one thing that just needed to be beaten. If I could beat this then I was going to be able to stand straighter and stronger.

The one thing I was never short of was determination, whatever I did I did with plenty of that, from my fighting to keep my little toe moving, to my hop-walking, my determination was never a problem. But the frustration I went through was maddening. One minute I was moving the toe, the next I wasn't, then I was hop-walking, the next moment I couldn't even pull myself up to use the frame.

I went on whatever happened, never thinking that I would never be able to do them again, always saying to myself: Today was the day. If somebody called to visit us I would always tell them just what I had got back that day, if anything, no matter how small because to me it was everything and that was what mattered. This determination kept me going, full of the will to carry on, trying never to let my head drop too far, always wanting to win, and on some days I did win.

By October I was back to doing five hundred sit-ups with ease in one workout in the morning, listening to my music as I did them. This to me was never the problem, I was always fit and had a good "engine" to keep me there, I made sure of that. It was all the water infections that knocked me back and after each one I would have to start again.

I went to see a urology specialist, called Mr. Brown, at Tameside Hospital's new Urology Unit. I had test after test done and after them I was told that I needed an operation - a urethrotomy - which would be done at the earliest possible time. The operation couldn't be performed at Tameside Hospital so I would have to go to the Urology Unit at Stepping Hill Hospital in Stockport.

I was put on the waiting list and told to be ready, as it might not take very long for a bed to become available. Vest was out at the shops to buy me some pyjamas and some toiletries the same day. She was always the same, she never let the grass grow under her feet. She must have been a Brownie or Girl Guide as a kid as she was always prepared.

Talk about tempting fate! I got another water infection not long after and I was not too good, to say the least. I was trying to wash it out of my system by drinking plenty of barley and spring waters in the daytime and lager at the night.

I went to the doctor's to have my steroid injection and as I was leaving the nurse's room I went dizzy. I was really struggling, hanging on to the wheelchair for dear life in the corridor, and then I just slipped to the floor. I shouted for Eileen the District Nurse to help me.

She and Denise one of the receptionists had to help me back into my wheelchair. They asked me what had happened. I told them it was an accident and that I was just sorting out the bottom of my pants and slipped. Eileen was having none of it. She told me that I looked dreadful and that she thought by the look of me that it was something other than me just falling. She gave me this really firm look and went and told the doctor what had happened. When I saw the doctor I told her the truth, that I had a water infection and had gone dizzy. She gave me a prescription for some more antibiotics to help fight the water infection and told me to ease up.

I felt so down in the dumps having to have more treatment, once again through the infection. I felt as though I was never away from the doctor's and that people would think I was a malingerer - something that I'm not, no such thing! Our doctors, and the receptionists who worked there, were the best, they would do everything they could to help the people who go there to see them. I got on with them all, on first name terms, and, as usual, I realised I was being stupid - looking at things that weren't there. They wouldn't think any less of me.

After that incident in the corridor I was to have my injections at home twice a week on a Monday and Thursday.

Once again I was laid up because of the water infections and out of action for a few days. I was unable to do any real sort of exercising and this put me in one of my many moods. It seemed everything that I did I moaned at. Not just moaned about it, but went on and on about it for ages and the one thing I blamed the most was the house.

I was finding it harder to get about the place because of the amount of transfers I had to do. It was causing all kinds of pains in my shoulders and arms and I was unable to find any ease or rest from it.

I found that when I was transferring from my wheelchair to go to the toilet on the "Orient Express" my mood got worse. All the way up the stairs I would be saying, "I hate this place. I really do.".

I would transfer to the chair on the landing and go into the toilet moaning as I went, and maybe one out of ten times I would fall whilst I was trying to sort myself out. That did it! I would go on and on to myself saying things like, "This house will kill me!", or another good moan I had was, "At this rate I will never see forty.".

The true fact was I loved the place but it was hard, damned hard at times to get around, and the more I moaned about it the more I really thought that I hated it. But it was a fact, I was struggling to get about and I was having lots of falls and having to struggle to get up or have to have someone help me. That was the painful thing, having to be helped.

The only way that I could get up in the kitchen when I was on the floor doing my exercises was to crawl to the sink unit. I would pull my wheelchair to face me, then with one hand on the wheelchair and one on the sink unit, pull myself up to a kneeling position then push up with my arms and turn ending up sitting in the wheelchair. I was very good at this and made it look easy. The lads tried to do it many times but they always ended up using their legs somewhere along the line.

If I ever fell in the house when Syl wasn't in, and that was a quite a few times, I would have to crawl. If I was upstairs in the toilet then I would have to crawl to the stairlift and pull myself onto that. Or if I was doing one of my hop-walks from the lift to the kitchen and fell then I would end up crawling the rest of the way and pulling myself up at the sink unit.

All this took its toll on my arms and knees and they were sore, very sore some days. This was why I was moaning. It was getting to be too painful in so many different ways.

We got to December and I was still waiting to hear from the hospital about the operation that I was to have on my bladder. I got worried, not over the operation, that didn't bother me one bit, it was the fact that it was getting near Christmas and there was all the shopping for presents to do and, more importantly, at the time there were still football matches I wanted to go to. I went to every home match of Manchester City and there were a couple of big ones still to play that I didn't want to miss.

On the eighth of December, Zac was born. He was the son of our Nick and his missus, Jeanette, so that called for a good few drinks to celebrate his birth. We did just that.

Then not long after, just a few days, I got the letter I had been waiting for from the hospital. I was going in on the twentieth; I went panic-stricken: what if I wasn't out for the Chelsea game on the Saturday? Syl got all my things ready and we went shopping for the last few bits that I would need to take with me.

Well it was the night before I was to go into hospital and we were talking about this and that and how good things would be after the operation. I never slept. I wasn't worried, just a little anxious. (Hmm! We do know!)

On the Thursday morning I went into hospital. Syl came on to the ward with me as usual. As soon as we were shown to the bed, Syl started to unpack my gear and sort out the locker at the side of the bed. I am always the same when I have to go into hospital. I get a bit emotional at having to leave the family, so I told Syl, 'When I go to the loo don't be still sat on the bed or outside the door, as you normally are.'

I gave her a kiss and told her that I would see her that evening when it was visiting time and not to worry as everything would be fine. I went to the loo and for once she did as I asked her to. She wasn't still sat on the bed, or stood smiling waiting for me as I came back out. No, she had gone and for once I wished that she hadn't listened to me and had still been there.

I got down to sorting out where things on the ward were, like the phone so that I could make a few calls to family and friends later in the day. The nurse came to take my temperature and blood pressure and we had a chat about how long I was going to be in for. She said that it depended on the individual and how they responded after the operation so I was no better off. I just wanted an idea so as I could sort out whether I would be out in time for the match on Saturday at Maine Road.

I got talking to a couple of blokes on the ward and they were in the same boat as me. They had been having problems with their bladder for ages, too. I was amazed at the ages of the people on the ward. It was a very mixed bag, people of all ages and in different health, fit and walking, young and old. I don't know why but that surprised me.

We got talking about football and me going to the match every time that City played at home. They asked me the same old questions why, then one asked how I got there. I told him that I drove in my car and took my son Gary and our Nick, who, once we got to the ground, got my wheelchair out of the boot and I did the rest.

They thought that it was great me going to the match and wanting to get out in time for the Saturday. They all said that I had no chance of doing it, though.

The ward was one of two for urology patients - one had closed for Christmas, as they were not admitting any more patients. And guess what! The one they had closed was the one which was geared up for disabled. So, some things, like the toilets on this ward, I found very difficult to use as there was no room to get my wheelchair in. The staff were great with me, though. When I needed to go to the loo they would help me all they could.

Syl came at the night with the lads, and she told me that our Moie had phoned to see if everything was OK. She was in the USA on holiday.

Syl asked me if I was nervous about the operation the following day. I told her I wasn't, I just wanted it over and done with so as I could get back to normal.

When visiting was over I went to the corridor with Syl and

the lads and watched them leave. This was the hardest time for me, saying goodbye to my family. I went back to the ward and got into my pyjamas ready for bed but there was no sleep in me that night. Not because I was worried or anything, no - there was this man who snored.

It was an unbelievable thing. What a noise! I thought we were near the zoo and something in there was making the noise. There was a really loud snort followed by a sort of whoosh and a 'Oh! Oh! Oh!' It was like the mating cry of an animal.

Then there was this old man who kept getting out of bed, the nurse would put him back in then a couple of minutes later he would get out and start again. The night flew past and it was the day of the operation.

Everyone who was going to have an operation that day wanted to be in the morning bunch and I was no exception. I wanted it over and done with so I would have a better chance of getting home sooner and getting back to normal, plus I really wanted to get to the match.

Well, there was movement down at the bottom end of the ward. They had already taken a couple of patients out for their operations just after breakfast and they were soon back. I kept asking the nurse when it would be my turn to go and have my operation. She just gave me the same answer - she didn't know.

I was talking to the man in the next bed to me who was also waiting to have his operation done when the anaesthetist came to see us. He sorted out the man next to me then came to see me. He asked me if I was nervous about the operation and, if so, did I need a pre-medication. I said that I was OK and that I didn't need anything. He said that there was a bit of a list that morning for the operating theatres so he could not say when I would be going down. Well dinner passed and I had been to empty my bladder about three times using the catheter but there was nothing to empty. The last time I went to the toilet I just wanted to be sure that I didn't take short on the way to the theatre, my nerves about that were terrible. Then my nerves really did start to twitch. I had the last-minute, "Oh, what-ifs", plus I was really gagging for a cup of coffee. All the people, who were not having operations or had had them, were eating and drinking and I was watching them doing it.

There was this one particular bloke on the ward who really

got up my nose. He would come round to people's beds and ask what they were drinking, or what it was they were eating. The guy was a scrounger. He had plenty on his locker but he was the type who didn't share, he just liked other people's. Well this guy came up talking to me and I could see he was after something, he had this silly smirk all over his face.

He had already been round the rest of the ward talking to those who were about to have their operations and he was coming away with loads of stuff. Now it was my turn to listen to all his crap.

The previous night I had been talking to an old guy across from me and he had given me some of his Old English Lemonade. The scrounger had seen us drinking and having a chat and you could see he wanted some, but he never came over to us, as the old guy didn't like him. I wonder why?

The scrounger asked me how I felt and was I worried. I told him I wasn't; I just wanted it over and done with. He then waffled on about all the operations he had had in the past and how there was nothing to it. That was it! This guy was an old hand; he knew everything about everything. He must have had every illness known to man in the past and he was now telling me all about them.

Then the conversation got round to the lemonade that I had been drinking with the old guy the night before. I told him that it was lovely and it had been a long time since I had had anything like it. Well the old guy had gone down for his operation and his locker was all on its own. Standing right out on the top of the locker was the lemonade. The scrounger asked me if I thought the old guy would mind if he had a quick sip. I told him he wouldn't and that there was a small cup of it on his locker.

With that the guy did no more than go over to the locker, pick up a cup and begin to drink from it. After a few moments his face turned a funny colour, with a sour look on it, and distorted.

He wiped his mouth and walked back over to me. 'That lemonade was really sickly,' he said.

'Oh, that wasn't the cup with the lemonade in you just drank, that was the cup the old guy spits in,' I told him.

Well this bloke ran off in the direction of the toilets without saying a word.

Because of all the lying down my legs were more numb than usual that morning. I needed a good loosen up and a stretch on the floor but there was no way that I could. I found that I was like a fish out of water in hospital. The bed I was in was difficult to get in and out of, even though it had been lowered to the height that I wanted. I was so used to my own bed at home. I could transfer easily on or off that one as I used the bedside table to help me. Also, the chair I used upstairs at home was different from the one I was using in hospital. I never thought that I would have any problems; I thought that I could manage anything that was put in front of me. Wrong! I was so used to the things that I used at home I just took it for granted that it would all be as easy when I was in hospital.

Well, the thinking and the wondering about what was going on soon turned into a theatre trolley being pushed down the ward by a man in green wellies and all the operating room gear that went with them. My heart started to do the full range of beats from slow, slow to quick, quick, fast.

He came to my bed with one of the nurses and asked me my name. He then put me on the trolley and I was pushed down the ward with some of the blokes wishing me good luck. Have you ever tried to speak and smile at the same time? It doesn't work. I found that out. I tried, and what a load of utter nonsense came out of my mouth.

'Good luck, Gaz!' a man in his bed shouted to me.

'Ougha,' I spluttered back out.

He just sat in his bed scratching his head as I went out of the ward, wondering what the hell I had just said to him. It was only a short way to the theatres and I was put just outside in what was a waiting area with some other patients who were waiting for their operations. A doctor came over to tell me that they would soon be giving me my injections and after that I would wake up and it would all be over.

As I lay there on that trolley I just kept laughing out loud thinking about that guy on the ward. This nurse came up to me and asked if I was nervous. I said, 'No. A funny thing happened on the way to the theatre!'

After a few short minutes of talking to the nurse the anaesthetist came and gave me my injections and after he had tried a couple of times on each hand, he realised, to my relief, that he was finding it hard to get a vein. So, he sent for another doctor to have a go and thankfully this one had no problem. He got the needle in a vein in one go. I just wish that he had done it in the first place; it would have saved me some serious pain and bruising in my hands.

After that I remember nothing except coming round with a nurse asking me if I was OK. I was. I was just a bit groggy that's all. There were other people in there coming round, also. I was in the recovery room I don't know how long, then I was taken back to the ward where I was put back in bed.

I felt great; I was just a bit sleepy and quite a bit sore down below so I had a peep at what they had done, as you do. When they had finished the operation they had put a catheter in and it felt strange. I had never had anything like this one before. It was totally different from the sort of catheter I used daily at home. Mind you, I never had to wear them, I just used them as I needed to.

A nurse brought me a cup of coffee not long after I got back on the ward. It felt great, the first mouthful was sheer nectar. I hadn't had a drink for ages. I had a good sleep after that and woke up some-time later to the sound of visitors talking. I had a look round then I just went back to sleep.

I had told Syl not to visit me that night as I thought that it would have been a waste of time. It was a good job, too, as the next time that I woke was in the early hours. I could feel myself passing water and it was sore. It was like hot water, I was cringing with the feeling.

I had a peep under the blanket and there was some blood. I shouted the nurse and she took a look and told me it was nothing to worry about and it was a normal thing after this sort of operation.

The blood looked as though it was mixed with urine and when you first see something like this you think, "Hello what's this?". It was fine, though, no problems.

I was having a cup of coffee, which the nurse had made me, and turned to get something from the locker. I just forgot about the catheter.

'Ouch! Oh, shit!' I nearly shot through the roof; I thought I had pulled my insides out. First I started twisting and turning in slow motion, wracked in this terrible pain I'd just caused myself. Then I just lay there in bed for a few minutes, motionless: the tears of pain running from my eyes. I was so scared to move just in case I pulled the catheter again.

This wonderful nurse made me another cup of coffee and I lay there in bed, listening to the man across the way snoring and watching the old man do his rounds and the nurse putting him back in bed.

I asked for the catheter to be taken out not long afterwards and it was. I was given a bottle just in case I needed it. I had it at the ready all the time as it felt as though I wanted to pass water all the time and I could go at any moment.

It was soon morning and the day of the big match: City versus Chelsea, and I was feeling great. I asked the nurse if I could have a shower as I was going home soon. She told me not to count my chickens, especially after what I had done in the night.

But after a bit of persuasion she agreed to let me go and have a shower. I was great, no major problems, just the pain down below so I went into the other ward with the disabled facilities and had a very careful shower. It felt great; so did I. I was ready for anything now, especially going home. I went back on the ward with the nurse and got out of my nightwear and into my day clothes ready to go home.

I went to the phone, phoned a florists and ordered Syl a bouquet of flowers to be delivered that morning at home. The nurse came to tell me that Syl had been on the phone again that morning to see if I was all right. She had been phoning ever since the day before when I went for my operation to see if I was OK. I phoned her to tell her I was fine and to come and pick me up as I was coming home.

She asked me if the doctor had been to see me and told me that it was OK to go. I told her he hadn't yet but he would soon, and there would be no problem. With that Syl went into one of her long speeches and told me that she wouldn't be picking me up until I had the all-clear from the doctor.

I put the phone down after speaking to Syl, went back to my bed and waited for the doctor to come round to see me and all the other patients who were expecting to go home that day.

One of the lads on the ward who was waiting to go home came over to have a chat to me. He told me that I had no chance of getting out that day because they didn't let you out if you had been bleeding after the operation. He was trying to wind me up just to get his own back for one or two things I had done to him. I told him I was fine, that I was in good working order and I was going home.

Well we didn't have long to find out because he had no sooner said that than the doctor walked on the ward. It didn't take him long to get to me and as soon as he reached me I asked him if I could go home. He asked me how I felt and I told him. He looked at the chart at the bottom of the bed, looked at the Ward Sister and then said, 'Yes, I don't see why not.'

Well I was off in my wheelchair, like Billy Whiz, to the phone to tell Syl to come and get me. I was telling her all this and she was telling me about the flowers I had sent her at the same time; it was a right old conversation.

We finished on the phone and I went back into the ward to see who else was going home. There were a few but the lad who had told me I wasn't going to get home was staying in for another few days. He was gutted and so I tried to cheer him up a bit by telling him about the guy with the lemonade. He laughed his head off. He was really glad that someone had got him as he, like me, didn't like the guy.

We sat there talking for a while, then Syl walked on to the ward. I was already packed up and ready to go so I said my goodbyes to the lads then left the ward for the car.

I was feeling great until I hit the cold fresh air outside and tried to get in the car. Well, I thought I had just been kicked in the stomach. The pains inside me were terrible. I hung on to the side of the car as I tried to slip across from my wheelchair to the car seat. Syl and the lads had to help me get in the car and out at the other end when we reached home. I was in agony. One minute I was feeling fine, the next I couldn't even lift my head through the pain. There was no way that I could have gone to the match as the pain was just too much to cope with. So, the one match that I wanted so much to see, I missed after all!

We got to Christmas and everything had calmed down. The pains were gone after a few days and I was feeling fine. I was going to the toilet great now, just like years ago when I had no problems with MS. I had the feeling back and I could empty my bladder without any trouble. It really was worth going in hospital and having the operation.

We had our Moie, Nick and his missus, Jeanette, with baby Zac round on Christmas Eve for a few drinks and a get-together. It was very nice. We were talking about the benefits the operation had given me and how I wished I'd had it done a long time ago. It was so nice to be able to know again when I wanted to go to the loo, instead of that last-minute dash and worry, like before the operation.

And now I was back doing my hop-walking from the lift to the kitchen in the mornings and even on occasions one in the afternoon as well. I had to stop a lot of the crawling that I had been doing because my knees were now in total agony. Just a few yards crawling would cause me to have so much pain, pain that would last all day and most of the night.

Syl said that Michael Jackson had the moonwalk and he was good at it; but me! Well, I was better. I did the moon-crawl. She never stopped taking the mickey out of me when I did my crawling. I could cover at least five yards in about three minutes, and that was on a good day, a very good day. From the stairlift to the kitchen I was lightning-fast! The lads could pass me going into the kitchen for their breakfasts, then go back the other way to go out the front door before I had even reached the kitchen.

When I was crawling my bum would fall from side to side and it took all the arm power I had to stop myself from falling over or flopping backwards onto my bottom. Syl called me the "weeble-wobble" and made jokes all the time, which helped, as a little laughter goes a long, long way in easing the pain.

I had now really slowed down and I had lost so much over the years, but I was still able to get about in one way or another, my willpower and determination made sure of that. The one thing that I had not lost was my sense of humour; that was still as good, if not better than ever. And there had been times this year that I'd found things hard to laugh at; mainly the pain but I did it, as it was the only way I knew how to cope with my MS.

Chapter Twenty

1996. A new year, a new start, but still the same old problems. There was one big change to my life, though - my bladder. That was fine and wasn't part of the problems. No, the main problem was still the terrible pains I was getting in my leg and ankle; they were getting worse.

It seemed that I just couldn't shift this awful, constant agony and God knows how I tried over the years. It was now restricting the amount of standing that I could do. I was down to doing something like one hour a day and that was split into ten minutes here, five minutes there. For the life of me I just couldn't take the pain the leg and ankle were giving out. I had no problem when I was on the floor doing my workout, it would just twinge every now and then and that wasn't too bad, but I couldn't stay on the floor all day, despite some days trying to.

The only thing I could do was try to ignore it and get on with what I was doing but once again that was hard to do, very hard at times. I found that the longer I sat in my wheelchair the more the pains would increase. I was getting on the floor and sitting watching the television at night with my legs stretched out in front of me to ease the pain before I went to bed. I was doing this several times through the day just to get a stretch on my hamstrings. I was trying everything that I knew to ease this pain but the pain was winning and I didn't like that. I hated to lose to this MS and this in turn started to see a temper in me that was directed at myself. The punches to my legs were getting more frequent, especially when I was having the pains or my legs didn't respond the way they were doing a few minutes before. My frustration was starting to show.

Vest and I loved to go out to eat once a week, for pub grub or a take-away and the pictures. This particular day we had done just that and I had some fish and chips from a chippy. Well at the night-time didn't I pay for it! I was as sick as a dog. I threw up for England, then I was on the loo all night. Syl got the doctor out and I had food poisoning. I'm such a lucky chap! I have this saying that if I fell in a bucket of boobs, I'd come out sucking my thumb. I just have that sort of luck.

I was laid up once again for another couple of days in the house and it drove me mad at having to stay upstairs near the toilet all day. I was so low in energy that there was no way that I could do any sort of exercising, or to loosen off my legs and they were in some need of a real workout. Syl was having to help me. Once again I was going in the direction that I had just come from. I was going to have to do some real hard work to get back to where I wanted to be.

Marjorie, one of the District Nurses came out to give me my steroid injection and I thought it best that I went back on a higher dose for a week or so, just till I got my energy back. So I did that. I went on a higher dose for one week and I was soon feeling a lot better and doing the things that I was doing before I had the food poisoning. But I was now really fed up with the house and the constant struggle to get up and down the stairs.

One night we were talking in the kitchen as I was making a drink and Adam said, 'If there was a fire in the house when we were in bed, how would you get out, Dad?'

We couldn't answer him. Oh we did give out this elaborate excuse but we didn't know what we would do if there was a fire. We just took it for granted I would get out. That did it! Syl said we were putting in for a transfer to see if we could get a bungalow. The ball was set in motion. We wrote to the council to see if they could help us and we got in touch with Kath Higgerson, our Occupational Therapist at Social Services, to see what ideas she could give us. Kath was great. She told us to write to some housing associations and ask to be put on their housing lists, as well as those of the councils and she got us plenty of names and addresses.

So I wrote to them asking to be put on their lists and Kath also wrote some letters to them, explaining our circumstances. We got lots of replies, some of them good, saying that they had bungalows but they were in high demand and that meant a long waiting list, and they worked on a points scheme - the more points you had the higher up the list you went.

Some other replies weren't so good: they just didn't have bungalows, or they were only for certain age groups. But at least we were on a few lists and stood as good a chance as anyone else. So now we had the moving bug and we went round looking at bungalows all around the area just in case.

Some of the housing associations that we had written to had property near where we lived and others in the Stockport area, which for us wasn't that far away.

We wanted, if possible, to stay in the area or as near as we could to it as the lads had grown there with all their friends. We didn't want to just move away leaving the lads having to start all over again at new schools and making new friends. Gary was leaving school in July, after he got his exam results, to start work, so that was another thing to consider.

If I was perfectly honest I loved the house that we lived in. It held so many good, and bad, memories for us, plus the neighbours we had were great. But it was a fact that I couldn't manage the stairs all the time that I needed to; just getting to and from the toilet in the daytime was the main problem that I had.

I asked Kath Higgerson if Social Services could build a downstairs toilet for us; that way there would be no need for us to move. But there was no way that they could have done it, they said.

There was the space out in the back but they thought that the house had been adapted to its full extent, so it would be best, in the long run, if we looked for a bungalow. I suppose she was right. I was getting worse because of my MS and the house, some days, was too much for me to handle. In fact, I was struggling just to get through the day some days but it was so hard to admit this fact, the fact that I was losing my battle to live in my home.

I looked around the house to see all the things that we had done to it and I started to think about all the things that had happened there. The lads had grown up there, they had never known anywhere else but this house to call home. They were too young to remember when we lived in Wythenshawe.

Then I looked at my Syl's face. I could see a hurt, a hurt I was unable to take away. She loved this house and had worked so hard to get it the way that we wanted it, but she was prepared give it all up and move away so I could have an easier life. This is love; love at its very best. She was, and is, my rock and through her I am the man that I am. I decided that if we had to move far away and the lads had to find new friends then I would take my chances and stay where we were and go on fighting the fight as I had been now for so long.

But we kept our fingers crossed and carried on looking around the bungalows in our area, hoping that we might, just might, get one of them. There were some in Stockport, that we looked at as we drove past in the car, which were very nice. I hadn't heard Syl so excited about anything for such a long time, not since we moved to the house we were in now.

Within a few weeks we were at it - we hadn't even been offered a place to look at, let alone move into, and we were looking at carpets and wallpaper. Talk about jumping the gun. We saw some bungalows that had just been built round the corner from where we lived and they were fantastic, just what we wanted but they were all taken. People were already happily living in them.

We were in April and Doctor Walton had given me some cortisone injections in my ankle to see if that would help, and it did. I got the first pain-free sleep that I had had in such a long time, but it didn't last for very long. Within a week or so it was back and with a vengeance, too. So much so that one day the pain was so bad that when I went to the toilet I stood up and don't remember anything else but finding myself on the floor.

Syl had a go at me. She told me I had to go to the doctor's to see about the pain and to get it sorted out, and quickly. I had been before and had tests done and there was no sign of anything, so what was the point of going and mithering about something that they had done all they could to find.

So I left it and just got on with what I was doing, looking for a new home for us to live in.

Over the year I had tried everything I knew to get rid of the pains in my right ankle and leg but nothing had worked for long or even, in most cases, at all. Then one day I was talking to this certain person about this and that and I just bent down to rub my ankle to try to ease the pain. This person asked me if I was in a lot of pain through it. I said I was and that there was nothing that I could do to ease it.

Well! That day the papers were talking about how some people with MS used cannabis to help them with their pain relief, and this person asked me if I had ever used it or knew anybody who had. I hadn't used it, nor did I know anybody who had, or at least if they had, they hadn't told me about it.

Well, to cut a long story very short I was given a cannabis cigarette (joint) to try out and see if it would help with my pain and with that I took it home.

Syl and I were frightened to death at the thought of having this thing - this "joint" - in the house. All day we were expecting the front door to be knocked down and a pack of sniffer-dogs let loose on us any minute. I said that I would try it in the kitchen when the lads had gone to bed and everywhere was locked up for the night. The day seemed to just drag on and on and it seemed the doorbell never stopped ringing we had that many visitors or people canvassing.

And every time we thought, "Oh, God this is it! We've been grassed over the grass.".

Well the night-time didn't come fast enough. We watched TV with the lads as normal but we were both looking at the clock, watching the time, hoping the lads would just get tired and go to bed. Then they started to do the lolling about that they do when they got tired so I told them that it was time they were in bed and off they went. As soon as the lads were in bed, Syl locked the house up.

We waited about a half an hour until we thought that the lads had gone off to sleep, then Syl and I went into the kitchen. I wheeled myself to the side of the sink and Syl closed the blinds, then got the cannabis joint for me.

I was shaking. I didn't know what to expect. For one thing I hadn't smoked in ages, and two, this was all new to me - smoking cannabis. I leaned over the sink and lit the joint. Syl was standing next to me with an air-freshening spray in her hand. I took a drag from the cigarette and held the smoke in my mouth for a few seconds, then I inhaled it.

Psst!

'What's it like?' Syl asked me.

'Cough! Cough! Cough! Gasp! It's OK. I think?'

Psssssst! Psssst!

'Can you feel anything yet?'

'Cough! Splutter! Choke. No!'

There was this smell. A strange smell. A smell that was sweet, yet tobacco-ey. I took a couple more drags.

Psssst! Psssst!

'Anything yet?' Syl asked, with this air of expectancy.

'Cough! Splutter! Choke! My head feels strange,' I replied.

'It must be the cigarette,' Syl said to me as she put her hand on my shoulder.

Psst!

'Wow, Syl, I feel very strange,' I murmured in this warty way. Then I went very, very light-headed, like the first time I ever had a cigarette. I thought that was the reason for it; that and the effect of the cannabis. Wrong! No, every time that I took a drag of the thing, Syl sprayed the air-freshener just over my head. I was inhaling that at the same time as the cannabis.

Within a few minutes I had gone totally light-headed and I had the feeling of being drunk. Syl threw the cigarette down the sink and flushed it away. I made my way to the stairlift to go to bed. I was floppy, in fact I was very loose. I was just about able to stay upright in my wheelchair. It was as if I had taken lots of Baclofen loosening tablets.

When I started to transfer from my wheelchair to the stair-lift I was so loose, I slipped off the lift and ended up on the floor. It took me a while with Syl's help to get upstairs and into bed where I had the best pain-free sleep that I have had in a long, long time. Was it the cannabis that did it or was it the spray? Who knows!

Over the next few weeks we looked at the outsides of so many bungalows and in so many different areas that in the end we were so fed up with it all it wasn't true. Then in early June we got a letter from one of the housing associations asking us if we would consider a two-bedroom bungalow just around the corner from where we lived.

We couldn't believe our luck, a bungalow on our doorstep. That was just what we needed and would mean the lads wouldn't have to make new friends and Adam could stay at his school and Gary could carry on with the job he had just started.

But there was a drawback, a big drawback: the size. It was only a two-bedroom bungalow, which meant the lads, would have to share a room together. Would they, could they? They had never had to share a room in the past. They were so used to their own space. Put them in the same room for any length of time and they would just go off the deep end over the slightest thing. That was in a three-bedroom house with an upstairs and plenty of space. Would things work in the new home, a bungalow with limited space and us all living on the one level.

There were times in the past, well to be perfectly honest once a day, that they would argue at the top of the stairs over something and nothing and these rows would go on and on for hours. So, could they share? All we could do was find out. We had a good long chat to the lads about it and I told them that if they didn't like the idea of having to share then I was prepared to stay where we were and see if a three-bedroom bungalow turned up at a later date.

The lady from the Housing Association came to see us to tell us all about the bungalow. It sounded wonderful, everything we wanted plus it was adapted for wheelchairs, too. The lady told us that the bungalow was small and she thought that all the furniture we had in our house wouldn't fit in it. That hit us hard. It had taken us a long time to get the things we had and they meant so much to us in so many different ways.

All this started to put me off the idea. What was the point in moving? The size of the place, the fact that the lads would have to share, and now we would have to get rid of most of our home. I was losing interest fast. It was turning out to be something that I had wished I hadn't started to look into. The lady said that we should look at the bungalow first, then decide whether to take it.

There was someone already living in the bungalow but they were leaving in the next week so had given us permission to have a look around while she was still there. We went round to have a look at it with the lady from the Housing Association and she was right, it was small, a lot smaller than our house. The living room was about half the size of ours and the bedrooms were even smaller. The lads would have to have bunk beds, as there was no room to put two single beds in the room they were to share. Our room wasn't much bigger either, just enough room to get about in but we would have to get rid of so much of our old furniture to do it. The upside to it all, though, was the place was gorgeous and so easy to get around in my wheelchair with everything being on the one level. It would take so much pressure off my arms with not having to go up the stairs to bed or the toilet.

Syl fell in love with it. You could see that the moment she first saw it; so did I. But it was now down to the lads. Could they sleep in, and share, the same room and would they? This was the big question The lads took a good look round the place and we told them how their room would have to be in such a small space and asked them if they could live with that. They said without any hesitation that they could. That did it. Syl and I said that we would take it; we were so excited at this wonderful new home that we were going to move into. There were one or two things that would have to be adapted for me but everything else was fine. So within the next few days Syl got her redecorating head on and went to work looking round the shops and warehouses for wallpapers and carpets for the new home. It was going to be a busy time as we only had a few weeks to sort everything out in our old house and move into our new home.

Over the next two weeks we were running round getting things we needed for our new home and everybody in the family was lending a hand. I didn't have too much time in the day to do exercises or loosening up so I just did them when and where I could, and I paid for it. My MS went on overtime. It really started to pay me back for the lack of exercising. I was as stiff as anything at the end of the day. I could barely move most nights, I was just like an ironing board - stiff. There was no way, some nights, that I could shift it. I tried everything I knew, getting on the floor and rolling my legs from side to side, tablets and standing, a nice long hot shower, but nothing could ease the stiffness. So most nights I would just go to bed as stiff as a board and hoped that I would wake in the morning that little bit looser.

Through the daytime the adrenalin was rushing through me, I was so busy driving here and there and doing this and that so the stiffness never bothered me. But then as soon as I stopped, that was it. I was in trouble, big trouble. But it was great I was doing something again throughout the day and I was so busy I loved it. I had missed this sort of feeling for so long, the feeling of doing something useful and the feeling of working again.

Syl never stopped. She had no sooner finished doing one job

than she started another. Our Moie helped too, she was great. My uncle, Harold, was a painter and decorator and he did the bungalow right through for us. Our Moie had helped us strip the walls and clean the place right through.

One of the jobs I loved to do was stripping the walls. It was great to be able to do manual work again, and get rid of some of those pent-up emotions I had, by ripping down the old wallpaper. Stupid, I know, but it beat just working-out on the floor at the end of the day at home. Plus it got me moving. The lads did their bit too, they stayed out of the way and once in a while they did a bit of the stripping in their room. You know the type of thing - pull a piece of paper off, then lie down for an hour.

We had to get rid of so much of our furniture to family and friend because of the space. Now that hurt. To see the things that had taken us so long to collect over the years going to other people. Syl's friends bought a lot of things and we gave a lot to family but there were things that we just couldn't give away or sell, they meant too much to us, so they had to come with us and we would have to find the room.

It was near to the time for our move and Kath Higgerson had told the Council that she had a few families on her books that our house would suit down to the ground, people with the same sorts of needs as myself. They needed property that was adapted and ours had the stairlift, the roll-in, roll-out shower and there were other things that made it ideal.

Wrong! The Council already had a family in mind and they were moving in not long after we moved out.

The family asked us if they could look round our house so we let them. They were very nice people, they didn't know that Kath had earmarked the house for a disabled family, it was all news to them. All the things that were in the house, the stairlift, the adapted toilet, the ramp in the back garden would be taken out, as it wasn't of any use to the family that were moving in. What a total waste of time and money.

Well it got to the day of the removal. We were up at 5 am that morning, as we were so excited. Syl loaded her car up with bags of clothes and bits of glassware and took them round to the bungalow. I sat there in my wheelchair in the lounge looking round the house that we had lived in for so long, almost empty of the things that once meant so much to us. No more family pictures on the walls, no brasses that once gleamed out and made our home a home. No more tidiness or a feeling of family life, just a mass of boxes and furniture waiting to be moved to our new home. I looked round the house for a last time. I had no regrets about moving, as I had come to hate the place we once called home, but was I doing the right thing for my family? I was doing the right thing in Syl's eyes and the lads had said that they wanted to move, but was I right?

Our Nick came to move us. They loaded the van with our things and I got in my car for the last time on the drive and drove off, never looking back. This was the beginning of a new chapter in our lives and a good one, I hoped.

Chapter Twenty One

It didn't take that long for us to move into our new home, as most of our things had already been taken there over the last few days and were in place. It was now only the big furniture that needed moving - things like the three-piece suite and bedroom furniture. By eleven o'clock everything was in place, our new home was now looking more like a home. Everything was almost done, there were just the odd things to do like making the beds and cleaning up all the empty boxes, but all in all everything had gone well and we were in. All that was left to do now was to settle in.

The first night was strange, as you can well imagine. Being in new surroundings for the first few days was hard for me, as I was having to once again work things out. Things like transferring from my wheelchair into the armchair. I could do it quite easily in our old house but now I was here and, well, it was a bit of a problem. Then there was another problem, I had no room in the kitchen to get on the floor and do my usual exercises in the mornings. Things were hard but I had to adapt. OK! I couldn't get into the armchair that easily but there was no problem getting on the settee. And as for my exercise, I couldn't do them as I used to in the kitchen as it was too small so they would have to be done on the bed or on the floor in the living room.

I always liked to do my workouts on the floor. It was firmer than the bed and I could get more things done, but by being on the floor in these new surroundings I found just how hard it was to get back into my wheelchair. I was so used to doing my workouts in the kitchen of our old house and using the sink to pull myself up. It was all easy then but now, now I was lost. I was just like a fish out of water some days. There I was, thinking that I could cope with anything that cropped up and at the first real obstacle I was struggling. I had to look for something else, now, to help me get from the floor back into my wheelchair and there wasn't a lot. I ended up having to use the arm of the sofa and my wheelchair just as I had done with the sink in the other house: a different method but the same result. I found it very difficult doing this for the first few weeks but in the end I mastered it.

It seemed that this new house, that I thought was going to be so wonderfully easy for me to get around, was really causing me more problems than I had ever had to cope with. Using the toilet and going to bed was totally different and harder to do. I was really struggling some days and it was starting to show. I was losing weight and not feeling too good; with all that and the pains in both my legs now, I was not in good health and to top it all off I got another infection.

Syl sent for the doctor who put me on a course of antibiotics and told me I had to stay in bed for a few days to recuperate. I was also prescribed something different, Zanaflex, to see if that would help me with the leg pain, rather than the Carbamazepine.

I slowly stopped the Carbamazepine and went on the new tablets but within a few days of stopping them I was in all kinds of trouble. The pain went from bad to worse. I never thought it possible how such a terrible pain could get worse but it did. I was in total agony.

I went to see the doctor who immediately put me back on the Carbamazepine, which took a few days to once again get back into my system and do what they had been doing. I thought that they had never done the job of easing the pain in the first place. It wasn't until I stopped them that I knew just how good a job they had done. Eileen, the nurse, came to give me my steroid injection and left me some vitamin drinks to try to see if they helped me. They did, with them and Syl's cooking I was back to my old weight and self in no time. I was all set to get myself fit. I was doing great and feeling fine with, for once, no major problems. I even got a few nights' sleep, thanks to a bottle of whisky, but just when you think that all is going well something happens.

There was trouble brewing in the house with the lads. They were having little rows that were spilling over into full-blown wars at times. It seemed that no sooner had we settled down in bed for the night than it would start. There would be a few words from their bedroom, you know, that sort of high-pitched talking. Then that would lead to all-out mayhem. There was no end to it some days and it was getting worse, much worse.

Through all this mayhem of arguments the house still had to have adaptations done. One of them was the toilet floor. The water from the level access shower wasn't draining properly and that meant the whole floor had to come up and be re-laid.

Then they had to put some handrails around the toilet, which would help me to stand up, and there were one or two more bits that needed doing in there at the same time. That meant we would be without a toilet for a few days whilst everything was being done and we weren't looking forward to that.

I had been having terrible pains in my stomach for a few days and I was finding it very sore when I went and passed water. I woke up one night with burning pain in my groin, my eyes were watering with the pain from it. I looked at the leg-bag I was wearing and it had blood in it. It was like when I was in hospital and had just had my operation.

I went to the toilet and Syl followed me. I took the leg-bag off, very carefully, and in the bottom of it was what looked like little stones and grit. Syl took a sample to the doctor's so they could send it off to be examined, which they did. After that morning of finding the blood I seemed to be pain free, the terrible ache that I had once had in my groin had gone and I was passing water as normal. I had to go for some tests as a result of the sample and at the end of it, it was thought that I had passed some kidney stones (ouch!). Never again, I hope.

We got a phone call from our Tony to say that his wife, Jane, had taken a turn for the worst. She had breast cancer. They had told us some months earlier. She was having treatment for it and everything was going fine until now.

We went down to see her and Tony at their house but she wasn't too well and the house was full so I stayed in the car whilst Syl went in to see her. Tony came out, with Richard and Colin (another of Syl's brothers), to talk to me and they told me how she was. She was in good spirits and doing well in herself, which was nice to hear.

Tony looked rough. He looked tired and wasn't sleeping, he was worried about all the treatment Jane was having. She had just come out of hospital after a course of treatment and now the nurses were coming out daily to give her more.

Syl came back to the car to tell me that Jane was doing well and that next time I came I would be able to get my wheelchair in the house to see her. Then a couple of days later we got a phone call, in the early hours of the 27th of September, from our Tony to say that Jane had got an infection and was rushed into hospital where she later died.

We were totally devastated, Jane wasn't just a sister-in-law, she was a mate, someone you could laugh and joke with, someone who had a great sense of humour, someone we will all miss terribly.

She was cremated on the 2nd October. All her family and friends were there, and Jane had so many, many friends because she was that kind of person - a person you were proud to call your friend.

The family would be there for Tony and his two little girls, Caroline and Katie.

GOD BLESS JANE.

We went to see Tony and the girls quite a lot the few weeks after Jane's funeral. We took them all out for something to eat, and the girls to the cinema. Some days we just went to talk and be there for them. Tony was always there for me when I was ill and there was no way that I wasn't going to be there for him, even if it was some days just talking to him at the other end of the phone.

We had settled into the bungalow quite well and I was now finding it easier to get about the place. It was like being on holiday. No stairs to fight with when I needed the toilet, no transferring from chair to chair, it was great and my arms were feeling the benefit of it all. All those little niggly pains that I had in the other house were steadily going and I, for once, felt as though there was light at the end of the tunnel.

Then they started work on the toilet to re-lay the floor and to do the other jobs in there that needed to be done, it was bedlam. We were given a portable loo to use while the toilet floor was being done. It looked more like a large white pedal bin than a toilet.

We went out most of the day so we could use the toilets in the shopping centres and we had to do this for three days. It was really grim, I can tell you. The floor had been dug out so it made it very difficult to use the wash-basin in there. It was fairly easy for the lads and Syl to get to, but for me it was another matter. I had to make do with getting as close as I could in my wheelchair and stretching to reach the sink. And if I had to use the portable loo, which I had to at times, we had an uphill struggle just so I could relieve myself. It was sheer murder and it made masses of extra work for Syl to do. With that and the lads constantly moaning about not being able to wash properly or to use the loo it was a nightmare. We were glad when all the work was done and we were able to shower and use our own toilet again.

So now everything in the house was getting back to normal. I had to go to the dentist's for a check-up. I went in the surgery and as usual the dentist helped me into the chair. He was having a good look round my teeth and, as dentists always seem to do, he started talking to me at the same time. He said that I needed three small fillings so I asked him if they were "only small", and he said, '-ish!'

Well! I told him to just do them without giving me the needle to numb them first; he looked at me as if to say "are you sure?" but I just smiled and lay back. Well, talk about putting my foot in it. I knew I had said the wrong thing when the drill started. I began to slide down the chair but I did it in this really brave way. I was somehow still smiling and doing that "mumble-talking" you do as you are having your teeth done.

Then my leg started with the "bops". It was going twenty to the dozen. He asked me if I was OK. I gave out this little wimpish 'Ah!' and sort of nodded as he carried on filling my teeth, all the time slowly slipping down the chair. God, my eyes were watering and I was making these little whimpering noises in a soft voice - 'Oh! Oh! Ooh! Oh!'

When it was over I was almost at the bottom of the chair and back in my wheelchair I had slid down that much. He told me I was brave to have had it done that way because he wouldn't have done it if it were him. I thought that when he said they were only small fillings, he really meant that it wasn't that much of a job. How wrong I was. I went out into the waiting room to Syl, smiled, then went to the desk to make another appointment. When we went outside I yelled like hell. Syl never stopped laughing all the way home; then round the shops; then she wasn't happy with that - she told everyone she met what I had just done.

Next time I go to the dentist I'll make sure that if I need work to be done I'll have injections, gas, anything. No more "Mr.

Brave" for me.

Chapter Twenty Two

We had now reached December and the Christmas rush was on us, but there was no Christmas spirit in the house. It was more like a battleground at times. I don't want to go into detail as that would take a couple of books to write, so all I will say is that the lads were not happy, not happy with anything.

It seemed that we were arguing and fighting with them all the time. One minute it was Gary, the next it was Adam. We couldn't do right for doing wrong in their eyes. They were growing up and they wanted their space and we let them have it up to a point, but they wanted more, a lot more, more than we were going to let them have.

We had a small house, now, and we were, at times, in each other's way. There was no give and take on their part. It seemed, to the lads, it was always us who were picking if we asked them to turn the music down, or not to have too many friends in at once as there was no room in their bedroom. And, of course, if Gary had his friends in then Adam wanted his friends in at the same time. And when this didn't happen the trouble would start. It was ongoing with different things, day in, day out, with no end in sight.

We had days when everything went well, then we would get a phone call from school saying Adam was missing classes or he was in more trouble with the teachers. Or Gary would one minute have a job, the next he had walked out. So you get the idea - the trouble was always with us and I started to blame myself for it all and that had an effect on my MS. I started to go downhill fast. I would get on the floor to exercise and everything was going well, then some trouble would start and I would just stop and say to myself, "What's the point?".

I was losing heart in the things that used to keep me going. I didn't want to do anything except stop the fights between the lads. I was watching my family tearing itself apart and I was at a loss about what to do for the best. I had talked to them, shouted at them, grounded them; nothing worked because they didn't want it to work.

It ended up that I went into the shower room at night to have a wash and would just sit there in my wheelchair and cry. For the life of me, I couldn't understand their reasoning. We had always given them everything they wanted. We had always been there for them. They had the best that we could get them and now it seemed that that was all forgotten, and Syl and I were now, at times, just a couple of strangers to them!

When we were arguing with the lads they told us that we were the ones who never cared for them, we were in the wrong for stopping the arguments before someone got hurt and they were sick of living in this house and wanted out. I found it very hard to take watching all this, watching the abuse that Syl took from them and not being able to do anything about it because I could not get to them. But I sometimes did. I hit out at Adam. I could have hurt him and God knows how I didn't after what he said to Syl. It broke me up. I just went into myself. I was hurting so much inside that I could very easily have done something to myself, Christ knows I wanted to.

I saw my family in tatters and all I could do was blame myself for moving to this house. Perhaps if we hadn't moved then it would not have happened. Syl said that it had been boiling over in the other house and was just a matter of time before it did happen and, no, it wasn't the fault of the house.

But that didn't make it any easier to accept. I couldn't stop blaming myself and the way that things went over Christmas was unbelievable. It was one Christmas that will live in all our minds for the rest of our lives.

The wars never stopped all over that Christmas and New Year. The family was in tatters. I was at the lowest that I have ever been in my life. I could not get any lower.

So 1997 started off with me a shivering, babbling wreck. I would cry if anybody spoke to me about the trouble. I just couldn't hold it in.

I was so bad that I had to give in to Syl's wishes and go and see the doctors for some help. As usual our doctors were wonderful. Doctor Hussein, after a long chat, prescribed me something called Lofepramine to help me. I had told him how I felt and he suggested that I might benefit from some counselling. I had nothing to lose. I was now at the worst stage of my life, so I said that I would do anything that would help.

I had got my steroid injections down to twenty units a week by now: ten units twice a week and it had gone well. With all the trouble, I had them put back up to forty for a week to see if that would help me. My MS was making me the lowest I had been for a long time. I could no longer crawl and I was doing very little working-out, as I just had no go in me. I couldn't have cared less; I had totally stopped trying. No more was I trying to do my hop-walking and the pain I was in was unbearable at times. Through it all I was in a real mess.

I had to go and see Doctor Walton at Tameside Hospital and she said that I needed to go into the Y.D.U. at Rochdale for some treatment. I said that I would, so she organised for me to go in as soon as there was a bed available for me.

Then the trouble started up in the house again. The lads were at each other's throats over something stupid. Then again, what was new?

Talk about bad timing. I got a phone call from the Y.D.U. to say there was a bed available for me to go in and have some treatment. There was no way that I could have gone and left all the trouble with Syl to sort out, so I told them I could not come in. Syl went up the wall with me but it didn't matter. I wasn't going and that was that. I didn't care how much she went on at me, I wasn't going to leave her to sort out this trouble.

My Vest is great. She thinks that she can just switch off from it all but she can't. The lads really hurt her with what they said and did; so much so, that she was having to take Prozac for it, and had been for a couple of years.

So what was now happening in the house would be sorted out by both of us, as it always had been, and not just by Syl, even though I wasn't at my best.

After a couple of weeks I had to go to the doctor's for my counselling appointment. I had to see a lady called Marian. I was very nervous about it all and didn't know what to expect. I had tried all that day to find an excuse not to go, I was so embarrassed about the way I was when I spoke about the troubles. But I went and as soon as I met the lady she put me at ease. We went in one of the surgeries and she asked me what was the problem. That was it! I was like a tap pouring out tears, and how she could understand what the hell I was trying to say I will never know.

What an understanding person she was. She passed me some tissues, I was that bad. I nearly went through the full box. We sat there talking, well, I was sort of sniffling as I talked and Marian listened and gave me advice. After that first talk about the troubles I went home and felt as though I had lifted a load off my shoulders.

I was to have more counselling to help me and, to be honest, I really needed it. I thought at the time that I could have managed but I was wrong. I needed to talk it through with someone other than a friend or a member of the family, no matter how close I felt to them.

I started to see Marian on a regular basis and found that I was getting better with every visit. The amount of pressure that I got off my chest talking to her was unbelievable, to say the least. I was feeling more and more like my old self after only a few visits and the tears were now getting less and less and the smiling was coming back to my face.

I had got so much off my chest in such a short time talking about our life, but as I spoke about my MS I could feel myself clamping up again. It was something that I hadn't really spoken about with Syl, let alone anybody else, but I was finding myself talking about it openly for the first time.

I went home afterwards and told Syl what I'd told Marian about my MS. She was gob-smacked. We lay there that night in bed discussing it and I found that I was telling Syl more about the way I felt and how it hurt me to see her having to do so much.

Well, she started then and we were talking into the early hours. It helped us to understand each other's points of view. There were times in the past that I thought that it was wrong for her to be having to do the things that, really, I should have been doing but she just said, 'Oh, yes! Who's going to do it, then, if I don't?'

She was right. There were days that I could do things around the house and I did my bit in the garden, doing this and that to help her and I was also still doing most of the driving. But, she made me see her point and I made her see mine. It was really good we got it out into the open and the little, silly things that we would get wound up about started to disappear.

Maureen the physio-terrorist came to do some work with me and ended up sticking acupuncture needles in my head and back, to see about getting rid of some of the pains I was having. It's a wonderful thing and it doesn't hurt and they do work on most parts of my body.

Both legs now hurt so much with the nerve pain and, to be honest, neither of them worked. I found it very hard to do any crawling as my back just flopped over to the side and it was so hard to drag my legs. But it never stopped me. I kept on and on trying to do it. There was no way that I was going to stop. I would once again master my crawling then I would build myself up to being strong enough, once again, to stand in the toilet. That was something I was planning to do, but like me I had to give it a go after only a few weeks.

I had been having to take more muscle-loosening tablets, Baclofen, to see if it would relieve the spasm in my leg muscles but they were making me floppy. I used to stand up using the spasm in my legs but now they were so loose it was untrue. This made it very difficult and very dangerous to do but I kept on trying till I did it.

Just like everything with me I no sooner get one thing back than something else started to play up. I had to go for a test on my bladder because it was not doing as well as it had been. I had to have this camera on the end of a tube inserted. I didn't mind the camera, it was the lights, lighting crew and Director that were painful. No, everything was fine it was just that I wasn't drinking the right stuff again, which I soon put right. I was drinking too much coffee and tea and not enough juices, that was all but I soon remedied that.

April was on us and it was nearly Vest's fortieth birthday, so I had planned something special for the day for her.

I had ordered a birthday cake for her from a local shop that specialised in novelty cakes. It had a woman in blue jeans with a white top, vacuuming up the number forty. Syl is so houseproud it is untrue, so I thought that this would be ideal for her as her surprise cake.

Besides the cake I had ordered a bouquet of flowers for her and some other little bits. Now, the cake and the bouquet had to be picked up on the morning of her birthday so I took her to Hyde to pick up the cake, as she knew I had ordered her one, but she didn't know what it had on it. All she was expecting was a plain old cake.

Well, when she saw it her little face lit the shopping centre. The people in the shop, and others who were just passing by shopping, all stopped and had a look at it and passed comments about it. Syl was over the moon. Then I said that I fancied a cup of coffee in the café that we used, so we went.

To get to the café we had to pass the florist's. They were waiting for us as we passed. I stopped and the lady passed the bouquet to Syl. Her face as this happened was one that I will never forget and for once she was stuck for words, which is very rare for Syl.

Everything that I had planned for that morning went well. It had taken me a while to organise and a lot of sneaking about behind Syl's back but I did it. Then just as she thought that there could be nothing else to surprise her, at dinnertime I got her mate to call in and I took them both out for a meal. Syl loved it.

The day went great, then at the night-time when the lads came in I took us all out to Fatty Arbuckle's for another meal. If anybody deserved pampering on their birthday it was my Vest. That's what I had saved up for ages to do and that's what she got, a special day. It was so nice that night, the four of us going out for a meal and there was no arguing from the lads for once.

May came and I was down to ten units of my steroid injections a week and doing well on it. Doctor Sambrook had left, so he was no longer my specialist. Instead there was a new doctor taking his place called Doctor Dicks. I had to go and see him and he thought that it would be better if I could come off the steroids, once and for all, and see how I went on. So I did, I finished off the last of the bottle we had started, which was only a couple of injections, then I stopped them completely.

It was going to be so strange not having to have them any more. I was so used to having them and for so long. I was quite worried because I just didn't know what to expect. I had been given them as a last resort as there was nothing else to help me at the time, so how was my body going to react?

I was told that if it didn't work for me, coming off the steroids, then I would have to go straight back on them and carry on from where I left off. I got the District Nurses some chocolates, as they had been so good to me over the last couple of years that I'd been on the injections.

Now, after so long, all I was having was the tablets and really I was glad. I wanted, if it was possible, to also cut them and try to live my life without any kind of medication. That would be very hard to do as they did ease the pain a little.

I went for one of my appointments with Marian and we were talking about my MS and the things I had got up to over the years, as there were some very funny stories I told her. She thought that I could share them with others and she told me to write a book about my life living with MS.

So I thought, "Why not?" and we talked some more and I went home and told Vest what I was thinking of doing and she was all for it, too.

So that night I got a writing pad, made myself a cup of coffee, went into the kitchen and started to get rid of some of the stress that I had kept locked away for fourteen years.

It was so easy. I had never talked about it so as I was writing it all down it was as though I was living it again, and it just flooded out onto the paper.

Well my handwriting is something that's left to be desired, even I can't read it, so Syl told me to go and get a cheap typewriter, which I did. I was there using two fingers, tapping away at the keys and then it was, 'Oh, Syl, Syl how do you spell *******?'

She went potty at me asking her to look up a word in the dictionary all the time, then after a couple of weeks we met Denise, the secretary from the doctor's. She was shopping on Hyde market and we stopped and had a chat. I told her about me trying to write a book and that I was having a hard time trying to type and my spelling wasn't up to scratch, in fact it was terrible. She said that she used a word-processor at work and that that just might help me with my spelling.

I was really interested in what she had just told us. It sounded just the thing I was looking for. Syl told me to go and have a look at the price of them in the shops, so we did just that. We went to Ashton town centre to price them up. They were quite dear in some shops but in others they were quite reasonable. There is always one salesman when you walk in these big shops who makes a beeline for you and asks you if you need help, and as soon as you say, "yes", that's it. Then, because you don't know too much about them, he tries to sell you something that is well out of your price range and tells you that this is the best thing since sliced bread.

There were so many to choose from and with so many different features that I was lost as to what the man in the shop told us. In the end we plumped for a certain one, one that we could afford and not too technical.

I couldn't wait to get it home, it was great. It made this noise every time I spelt something wrong. You should have heard it bleeping.

Then the inevitable happened. Just as things start to go well there is always something in the wings waiting to go wrong. It was me. I started to go downhill fast. I thought that it was because I wasn't on the steroids. I had no strength and I was starting to get the pains back in my arms. I just couldn't lift them.

I ended up being quite ill. Syl sent for the doctor and I was given a short course of steroid tablets to help me. I wasn't well for a week or so then I started to, slowly but surely, pick up.

Maureen, the physio-terrorist, treated my shoulder with acupuncture and it seemed to work well. Besides that, Doctor Hussein gave me an injection for my tennis elbow and within a few days I was ready to go again.

I was still seeing Marian and I really was on the mend. I had gotten rid of so many things from my past through the writing. I had spent fourteen years of my life with so many different feelings. I hadn't lost them. I had just shut them away at the back of my mind. I had been carrying them with me and I was too afraid to admit to myself that I was scared and worried from day one. It had been easier to hide them than to face them and talk about it to somebody, until now. I was still the same person, I just talked more about the things that I had been so very scared of: my MS. I was so scared that through it I would lose my family and friends I didn't want to appear weak.

Whilst I had been writing over the past few months I had really let my fitness go. I was not paying attention to myself through this and the trouble that was constantly brewing in the house. One minute it was great, the next - trouble with huge arguments over school and now some really undesirables that the lads wanted to mix with. This had all taken its toll on me.

If this had happened a few months earlier, I wouldn't be writing this book. But now I was back, the determination was there again, and this time I wasn't going to let it go so easily. The lads were still at it but this time, instead of me falling apart, I sorted it out. And

I did. I threw Gary out, even if it was only for the one night and he went then to his mate's house, partying.

It was hard but it had to be done for the sake of peace in the house. I was trying to prove a point to them that we had had enough of all the crap they were giving out to us and to show them that we were going to take no more of it. All that particular day they'd been out for trouble and it was terrible. Something had to give, and on this occasion it was me doing this to Gary.

Don't get me wrong, I love my sons with all my heart and I would do anything for them, that will never change, but there are times when I don't like them very much!

What I had done for the sake of peace in the house really hurt me to the soul. I was hurting with a pain that just wouldn't go away. Gary had spent one night away from home because of it all, yet I was the one who felt as though I was at fault. For a few brief days it had seemed to work. There had been something that resembled peace in the house. The lads were civil to Syl and me and they were talking to each other instead of the usual screaming, but then after only a couple of days, and without any reason, it all began to start over again.

Throughout it all I went on one of my fitness spurts. I wanted to get fitter quicker than I had been doing, so we bought one of those exercise machines that tighten up your stomach, the ones where you lie on your back on the floor and do sit-ups and after only a few weeks you get a six-pack. Well, I already had a six-pack. The trouble was, it was still in the box!

I was doing five hundred various types of exercises with the machine in no time. It was really good. Syl had gone on a fitness drive, too as she wanted to lose a bit of weight, so she was doing her exercise along with me.

My fitness was back once again and to a good level. I was feeling good. I was close to my fortieth birthday and Syl had something special planned for me; it was the birthday that I had said for a long time that I would never reach.

I didn't know what to expect. Syl and the lads had put banners up outside the house saying "Happy Fortieth Plus!". She had got me this fantastic birthday cake. It was a man in a wheelchair fishing. That was besides all the lovely presents she and the lads got me. I was really lucky. Our Moie and Nick bought me a gold chain and had arranged to take the family and me out for a meal to a local pub. What a day we had. It was fantastic. To have all my family together was just the thing I needed, and to top it all Moie's friend, Maria, drove down to where we were with a bottle of Jack Daniel's bourbon for me.

This had been the birthday I thought I would never reach, but now that I had got there it was the one that would start my life. They say that life begins at forty and believe me it will.

After the hype of my fortieth birthday it was back to the old routine. For a few days I had hardly any pains in my legs. In fact they had given me a holiday. But now they were back and this time with a vengeance. The pain in my legs was now at an all-time high and I could not sleep, even with sleeping pills.

As soon as I got in bed the pain would start and my feet would go into a spasm. It was like someone trying to bend them the other way. The pains were so violent and coming from my ankle, as normal, but now they were also in my left knee and hip.

I would have to sit on the side of the bed most of the night just to get some peace from the pain. Syl would get up and make me a coffee and try to help me by massaging and stretching my legs and ankles but the pain just wouldn't go, whatever we did.

I would take four Baclofen muscle-relaxing tablets one hour before I went to bed to stop the stiffness, and four Carbamazepine nerve tablets as well, just to ease the pain. I should have had no problems in sleeping really, taking all these tablets. They were in addition to the ones I took in the daytime.

I needed to be doing more leg-work to help me with this pain, as the more movement I got in my legs the less the pain was. But there was no way that I could do the sort of exercises that were needed unless I was able to walk.

I had seen this fantastic machine in a magazine. It exercised your legs whilst you sat in your wheelchair. It was just like a mini exercise cycle, without the wheels. You put your feet in the pedals and they would go round whilst you remained in your wheelchair. Fantastic! Oh, to be able to use something like this on a regular basis would be magic. I wish there were places you could go to and use these sorts of things. I, for one, would never be away from them. The machine would help with the stiffness and the pains in my legs if they could have that sort of movement on a regular basis.

Chapter Twenty Three

September came and I started at college doing a course on keyboarding. It was great. I was doing a ten week course and at the end of it there was an exam. I was in a class full of secretaries who wanted to learn about computers, as I did. Now, these women were fast when they typed. They could gab to their mates next to them and still get the work done in rapid time.

Then there was little old me using the one finger on each hand and constantly looking at what keys I was pressing. But when it came down to using the computer, well, we were all as slow as each other. I loved it. It was so nice to be doing something that I thought I would never like doing.

A few weeks after I had been at college, I saw this advertisement in the paper about cheap, reconditioned computers. So I told Syl about it. I told her that they were better than a word-processor and they would be like the ones I used at college.

She knew I wanted to go and look at one of them, so we went to Stockport, just to look, you understand, nothing more. We went to the shop and had a look at them and told the young lady there what we wanted. She pointed out the one that would do that, plus hundreds of other things. I had a talk to Syl and told her that if I got a buyer for the word-processor then I would get one. So with that Syl put an advertisement in the local shop window and within a couple of days we got a buyer for it. So we went back to the shop to order a computer.

Syl said she couldn't believe it was me getting a computer, especially after all I had said about them in the past. I don't know why but my whole outlook towards them had changed since I had been using them at college and I thought that this just might open up new doors for me.

I had to go and see Doctor Walton about the pain in my legs, as they were now so bad that I couldn't do anything to ease the pain, plus I hadn't seen her in a long time. We had a good chat about them and I told her just how bad they really were. She said that she would like to try me on a new treatment using something called Botulism!

Well, my bottle went. I looked at her, all worried-like, as I thought that this was supposed to be poisonous. Well it is, but using it a certain way was quite safe and they were using it to great effect to stop stiffness in other people. We sat there discussing it for a while and she told me all the benefits that the treatment had, how safe it was and, if I wanted to try it, it would be injected into my leg to, hopefully, stop the pain and the twisting and turning.

Well that was all I needed to hear. I was all for it. I would have had it done there and then if I could have, but it had to be ordered, so I was going to have to wait a little bit longer. Doctor Walton told me that she would send an appointment out to me to go as an outpatient to the Y.D.U. in Rochdale as soon as possible.

Syl and I went home that afternoon with plenty to talk about. She really was very nervous about me having this done but it sounded great, this Botulism injection. For the first time in a long time I was thinking that I might just get rid of these terrible leg pains once and for all.

Our Tony phoned that night for his weekly natter and to find out how I went on at the hospital. As soon as I told him about it the first thing he said was, 'I'll take you there when you need to go.'

That's our Tony he is really good when it comes to being there.

'Oh, cheers, Tony. That's good of you, mate, to do that,' I said.

'No bother, Gaz. I want to hear you scream in pain!' I won't tell you what I called him over the phone, but you can guess.

It only took a week or so for the appointment for the Botulism injections to come through. Tony was at our house about nine thirty, just after dropping the girls off at school. He was full of it, trying to wind me up about the Botulism, telling me it was poison and that this would be my last day. He's got a warped sense of humour at times, has our Tony. But it seemed to make him happy, bless him.

We had a quick brew then set off to Rochdale. Now, we have been to the Y.D.U. lots of times but can I tell you where it is? No! Tony knew, or so we thought, as he had been with us many times in the past. Well we were on our way and everything was going well, until he started to get that look on his face. A look that was total blank! Now, that's not a strange look for him, but this time we knew there were problems.

The man next door to where we lived had drawn us a map just in case, but did Tony need it? No! So we carried on and on until we got into Rochdale town centre. I told Tony that I thought it was another way, totally different than the way he was going. That was it. He went into his "bluff mode": 'I know, I know. You don't have to tell me. I thought it might have been quicker going this way,' he said.

Now, I had given up smoking a long time ago. I had stopped because I was getting a burning feeling in my legs. It was as if they were on fire and I would go dizzy after having a cigarette. But there were times, just recently, that I did have the odd one or two at the football match if my legs played up.

Well, this day I needed one. Not because I was in pain or because I was worried about the injections. No, I just don't know why but I had to have one, then another, just for something to do, I think! It seemed that we had been in the car for ages and it was almost time for my appointment.

We were going round and round the roundabouts, one after the other. It was wonderful to see Tony's face as he was trying to figure out just where we were. Then he started saying, as if to convince himself, 'I'm not lost. I know where we are going. I'm just looking for this, what's-its-name.'

We ended up stopping at this shop and asking directions. Now this might surprise you but we were nowhere near the hospital. No! It was the other way and we had passed it several times, so we went back the way we had come, round and round the roundabouts. I waved to a few people. Tony asked me if I knew them. I said, 'Only in passing, mate. Only in passing.'

That did it, he was gone! The tears were running down his face he was laughing that much. We got to the Y.D.U. eventually and we went in to see Doctor Walton. I was only going to have the one leg done this time. I went into this room and got onto the bed. I took off my boot and sock and had to roll up the leg of my trousers on the left leg as that one was the most painful.

There was Doctor Walton and another doctor who wired this machine to my leg, then they had to wait till my leg went into spasm so that the machine would show them the right muscle they were to inject. I had several injections in the leg, some just behind my shin, some in my calf, and the rest in my ankle.

A screen had been pulled around the bed and Syl and Tony were outside it, listening to what was going on. Doctor Walton asked me if I could move my foot for her, so she could get the machine to pick up the right muscle. Well I couldn't move it by myself as the muscles didn't work, so the other doctor helped me and every time he did I said, 'Thank you.'

When the injections were done, Doctor Walton told me that it might take a couple of weeks before they started to work and that they would last roughly three months. I put my sock and boot on then we went for a coffee.

As we were having the coffee Tony started saying, 'Thank you! Thank you!' all the time. Him and Syl had been giggling away and laughing at me saying, 'Thank you'.

They asked me why I was saying "Thank you" every time I had an injection. I told them why but it made no difference. All I got from then on was, "Thank you! Thank you!".

It took us ages to get home. Tony knew another shortcut that took us to the moors and the surrounding countryside. It was a wonderful day out, wonderful.

THANK YOU TONY! THANK YOU!

After about a week the injections started to work, first in my foot, then slowly they moved up my leg to where I had had the injections. I had been having these terrible pains in my leg now for so long that I had forgotten just what it was like to be free from it all. But now here I was experiencing the delights of once again having no pain and it was so very nice to be able to feel my toes moving. This time I was doing it, not the twisting or the spasm - no it was me.

I was now able, albeit ever so slightly, to feel the joy of controlling my own toe movements once again. The awful burning and twisting pains I was having only a few days ago in my calf and lower leg were now totally at ease. I really was pain-free in the parts of my leg that had been injected. But from my knee up the rest of my leg was still the same. The spasm I was having in that part of my leg was still there and causing so much pain, mostly when I was trying to sleep at night.

Both my legs are usually very sore. It's as though the hamstrings at the back of my knees are too short. I really have to fight with them each time I want to straighten them out so I can lie down. If I try to sit on the floor with my back against the chair to watch TV I have the same problem. I have a real fight to get them to go straight out in front of me, so much so at times that Syl has to give me a hand. It's as though my body has taken the shape of me sitting in the wheelchair and doesn't want to change. I wouldn't mind if I just sat there in my chair doing nothing all day, I don't. I get out of my wheelchair to do my exercises several times a day, and I sit on the floor as often as I can. But it's always the same thing - a battle to do simple things.

Then, some days it would be that I had no sooner sat down with my legs out in front of me watching TV or doing a crossword, then it would start. I would feel myself going stiff, and I mean stiff. I would start slipping down the chair. It's as if someone's pulling me by my feet.

When this happened I would then have to fight to get hold of my ankles and pull myself forwards and just sit there holding on to them until the stiffness had gone.

I have tried so many different things to combat this. I've tried having the foot drop splints on to see if they would stop it, or at least ease it, but no. Instead, all that happens is that my feet try to push them off and that makes the pain a lot worse.

This Botulism is good and it is working. The pain I have had in this ankle, for over six years, has gone for now; as has the spasm and twisting. For how long, who knows? but whilst it's gone I can concentrate on the upper parts of my legs to get them stronger and fitter and I will win. There are no ifs, buts or maybes about that.

This is all I have been asking for over the years. Something to help me fight back, and perhaps now I will be able to get that sleep at night I've been missing, instead of having to sit on the side of the bed in pain.

It will be strange if the pain does go and the spasm is no more, as I have lived with it for so long now. I have forgotten what it is like not to have it there, to do the simple things in life, like going down the street in my wheelchair and enjoying shopping with Syl. It would be strange not to have to suddenly lunge forward in a crowd to rub the pain in my leg away, and scare the life out of someone. I've become used to having to try to put weight through my legs to stop them jumping up and down with the spasms. Some of those things going missing would be wonderful. They've brought me so much embarrassment over the years. To have some freedom from pain would open so many doors that have been closed to me for a while now. Freedom from pain would be a luxury that I have missed for so very long.

The last fourteen years of my life living with MS have been like a roller-coaster ride - one minute I was up, the next I was down. And throughout this time I have seen so many changes, and I personally have changed from the man I was fourteen years ago.

When I was first diagnosed as having MS I thought that my world had just caved in around me. I was only in my early twenties, keen, filled with a zest for life. I had a young family and a good job. I thought that I was about to lose everything because I had this terrible illness, this thing called MS.

I thought I wouldn't be able to do anything about it because there was no cure. Well that's what I thought that first night, as I lay there in that hospital bed with an empty feeling tearing at me from the inside. I was unable to walk properly and had this strange, numb, tingling feeling in my hands and legs.

I shed so many silent tears that night as I lay there, just trying to think of what was going to happen. I pictured my wife and two little boys in my mind, wanting it all to be a dream; a dream that would be gone when I awoke in the morning and I would be back in my own bed next to my Syl. But it wasn't a dream and I was going to have to face it. I now had this thing called MS so I was going to fight it and fight it with everything that I had. It wasn't going to get me on the cheap.

Syl had come to visit me later that day in hospital and we talked about what I had been lying awake thinking about throughout the night, and my fears for our future. She said to me all the things that I needed to hear. All the fears that I had just went into thin air. I should have known it right from the start that the two of us could cope with this thing that had been thrust upon us.

Over the first few years when things started to change and

my MS got gradually worse, I was naïve to say the least. I was going through bad times, physically, mentally and emotionally and I didn't know what to do for the best. But Syl was always there to hold my hand and to give me something that is stronger than any medicine - love.

I have tried and done so many different things over the past fourteen years in my fight with MS. Some battles I won, many I lost, but I never gave in and through it all I have tried to smile.

MS is a terrible disease and it takes whatever it wants when it wants, without giving a second thought to the person or to the consequences. One night you go to bed with your body working perfectly. Your family life is great, your world is one that you love, then you awake in the morning to find that MS has taken something from you. Something that you can not replace. Your world has now been turned upside down. The MS doesn't care and it will go on taking from you if you let it. But you don't because you have heart and so you fight back with every inch of your body, you fight back every minute of every day, you fight back to hold on to what you have. This is what living with MS is like.

There is, as yet, no cure for MS but there are two things that you have that MS can't take from you: your heart and soul. Only you can give them to MS, so you use them to fight back, and each day you win a little bit of the battle because your heart and soul was in it that day.

You only have to look around you and see family and friends there waiting to help you. Don't shut them out as it is so easy to do. It's their battle, too and they need to feel part of it so let them help in any way they can no, matter how small.

There have been many times when, looking back over the years, I've thought: "I wish I had done that, then.". And then there are the times I wished that I hadn't. But I think that on the whole, though, I have done all the things that I thought were right, and through it all I think I've done well. I'm fit, I am still able to drive my car, I go to football and I live my life to the full and that's something that will never, ever change.

I truly believe, in my heart and soul, that one day I will walk again so I will carry on doing the things that I'm doing till I get there.

Then, one day, you may see me walking down the street, or playing darts in a pub and you may say to me, 'How's it going, Gaz?'

And I'll say, 'Yeh, no problems!'

Over the years I have met some wonderful people. People who have helped me through some sticky patches, people who were there to lend a hand, people that were there just to listen, people who helped where and when they could. I would like to dedicate this little bit of the book to them.

To the doctor who spent so much time, when I was first diagnosed as having MS, explaining things to me. To Doctor Sambrook who, in the early years of my MS, treated me so very well. To my doctors now, who treat me from day-to-day and help in every way they can. To Doctor Walton, and all her team at the Y.D.U. I thank you all. To those people in the street who come up to me when I'm sitting in my wheelchair outside a shop waiting for Syl and ask me if I'm OK and do I need any help. To our doctors' receptionists and Bob, the chemist, and all his staff. To the District Nurses who have, over the years, looked after me so well. To all the different physiotherapists at hospital, who I have loved working with.

To Marian, who I will always owe so much to for helping me through one of the worst parts of my life that I have ever had and for showing me a new side to my life - a side that I never knew existed. Thank you.

There are just so many wonderful people that I have met over the years, the list is endless. But there are special ones in my life that mean so very much to me, like Maureen, the physio-terrorist.

Maureen has been treating me for many years now. She is a wonderful, caring individual and without her professional help and her caring touch I know that I would not be as good as I am today. Maureen treats me, not the disease. She knows just what I can and cannot do. I know that her dedication to her profession has kept me fit and strong and she is the one physiotherapist in a million. She is the Physio-terrorist!

To Stan and Edie, who I love like they were my own mother and father. They treated me like one of their sons and made their home my home from day one. For all their help and understanding over the years when times were hard, but especially for being a big part of my life. Thank you!

To all my in-laws, too many to name but they know who they are. They are there for me and have shared all my ups and downs over the years. Cheers to you all!

To Jane. A good friend who shared so much of her short life with us through her laughter and her tears, a person who I will miss for the rest of my life. Thanks Jane!

Then there's Tony. What can I say about him that I haven't said in this book? You can see for yourself just how close to me he is. He is a special brother-in-law and a very special friend. We have done so many things together over the years and some of the things that he has done for me I can never thank him enough for. He is a true friend, that's what makes him that special to me.

Then there are my two nephews, Nick and Tim. I used to watch over them when they were younger like a big brother and I saw them both grow into men with families of their own. Now, they watch over me. They do all they can when they can to help me and they still look upon me as their big brother, instead of their uncle. Thank lads!

To my big sister, Maureen - "Moie". Our kid is a very special person. I love her with all my heart. She has looked after me all my life and has always been there for me through the good times and the bad. Throughout the years we have grown up together and she has been my "big brother", fighting my fights for me. And now we are older, nothing's changed. She still fights my fights, only this time with me against my MS.

I know there's nothing that she wouldn't do for me and I know I only have to ask and she will be there for me. Knowing this means so much to me. I love my sister with all my heart and enjoy every moment we have together. Love you Moie!

To my mum, Peg. Throughout our lives my sister and I never wanted for anything as Mum always did her best to make sure that we had it. She gave us a wonderful life without asking for anything in return and she was always there for us, no matter what. When I was first diagnosed as having MS my world collapsed. I thought that I wasn't going to be able to cope with life. I forgot that I had my mother in me. She was always strong and did what she said she would, just like I do. For this I thank her. I miss my mum so much it hurts, yet I only have to think of her to know she is there with me helping me through the bad times and showing me the way. Words can't say what I want to say, Mum, so I will just say the words that I could never bring myself to say while you were here: I love you!

To my sons Gary and Adam. I have watched them grow into two fine young men and, sadly, they have seen all the things that have happened to me over the past fourteen years that I have had MS. I cherish every moment that I had in the early years, when I could still walk and play football with them. How I long for those days. Then I went into a wheelchair, but life never stopped. I was still playing games with them and we were still able to laugh and do all the things that we did. Now that they are older we go to football and talk about it on the way home. They are very protective towards me and watch everything I do. I see them when I am on the floor exercising and I struggle to get back into my wheelchair. Their faces say how I feel. I love my sons with all my heart and I know that I will walk again and we will play that game of football I owe them. I love you both! Up the Blues!

And finally to the one I've loved from the first moment we met all those years ago - Syl! She is my world, the one that I go to sleep at night with and thank God is mine; the one that has a smile that can light up the darkest room; the one that can put things right in my world with just a word. She has always been there at my side through thick and thin - through the good times and the bad; through the laughter and the tears, feeling all the pain that I felt, urging me on to do one more exercise on the days when I felt like packing it in. Dressing me when I couldn't dress myself, nursing me through so many different things, helping me to move my legs on the days that they were too stiff to move by themselves. These are just a few of the things that go to make my Syl. She is a very special person and I am so very proud to call her my wife!

Life isn't all doom and gloom having MS, as you have just read in this book. It's what you make it. I've been very lucky in my life to have around me the people that I have just mentioned. Through them I have lived a good life and will carry on doing so.

I'd never known my father and always wanted to find him. And in 1987, Syl did just that. She found him for me.

But that's another story....

Other Books available from CK Publishing:

Anne Droyd and Century Lodge

by Will Hadcroft

ISBN: 1-903674-14-X
£5.99

Gezz and her friends, Luke and Malcolm are minding their own business, having fun on the small area of wasteland near their homes when their lives are shattered by the arrival of a truck carrying a strange visitor who will change their lives for ever.

Anne Droyd and Century Lodge is the exciting first novel from Worsley-based writer Will Hadcroft. All the best features that made the Famous Five books such compulsive reading have been distilled and updated to produce a modern fable which entertains, surprises and amuses while also looking at how children see themselves and their place in the world as they approach adolescence.

It Never Rains in Italy

by David Critchley

ISBN: 1-903674-15-8
£5.99

After years spent shivering under dripping canvas in campsites North of the Alps, David made himself a promise that his next holiday would be spent in the sun. No more Bavarian mudbaths for him. They were going South. After all, everybody knows, it never rains in Italy!

This first book from Merseyside-based teacher, David Critchley, is a funny and touching tale of a long holiday in a country that seduces. This engaging tale tells how David and his wife fall in love with the place, the culture, and the people.